Welcome to
Drones
The Complete Manual

It's not too long ago that we thought of drones as
inaccessible technology, reserved only for the military and
professionals, but that's no longer the case. Commercial
drones are taking the electronics market by storm, which
has got many people excited. Drones are increasingly
being used in news broadcasting, filmmaking, emergency
aid, animal conservation, art exhibitions and entertainment.
If you're hoping to get creative with a drone too, getting
started might seem daunting. However, in this Complete
Manual, we make it easier than ever before. You no longer
need to be a certified pilot to fly, all you need is a drone
and this book, and you're ready for take-off!

Drones
The Complete Manual

Imagine Publishing Ltd
Richmond House
33 Richmond Hill
Bournemouth
Dorset BH2 6EZ
☎ +44 (0) 1202 586200
Website: www.imagine-publishing.co.uk
Twitter: @Books_Imagine
Facebook: www.facebook.com/ImagineBookazines

Publishing Director
Aaron Asadi

Head of Design
Ross Andrews

Production Editor
Sanne de Boer

Senior Art Editor
Greg Whitaker

Assistant Designer
Steve Dacombe

Photographer
James Sheppard

Printed by
William Gibbons, 26 Planetary Road, Willenhall, West Midlands, WV13 3XT

Distributed in the UK, Eire & the Rest of the World by
Marketforce, 5 Churchill Place, Canary Wharf, London, E14 5HU
Tel 0203 787 9060 www.marketforce.co.uk

Distributed in Australia by
Gordon & Gotch Australia Pty Ltd, 26 Rodborough Road, Frenchs Forest, NSW, 2086 Australia
Tel +61 2 9972 8800 www.gordongotch.com.au

Drones The Complete Manual First Edition © 2016 Imagine Publishing Ltd

ISBN 978 1785 462 962

Part of the

Gadget bookazine series

IMAGINE
PUBLISHING

Contents
What you can find inside the bookazine

Learn to fly your first drone

"Drones are both affordable and widely available. You just need to make a few choices when choosing one"

Getting started with your drone

Find out how to buy, fly and maintain your drone, as well as how to get involved in online and real-world communities worldwide

You might have heard of drones, but now suddenly you're able to buy them! There are so many practical uses for drones, and in addition, they're also fun devices to play with.

With great fun comes a great range of choices to make. Quadcopters, multirotors and unmanned aerial vehicles (UAVs) are serious tools with specific uses and benefits. Every type has different advantages and disadvantages, but they all share the same issue of security. You also need to learn how to fly your drone, and understand what it is capable of.

Once it is airborne, you could fly your drone up to check out storm damage on your chimney, for example, or check out those hard-to-reach ledges and gutters without spending money on scaffolding. You can set up the drone so its cameras send you live images. They can also record, though, and in remarkable quality right up to 4K. Imagine replacing dull estate-agent photographs with a two-minute flyby around your house. All this is now possible because of recent technological advances, such as lightweight but strong materials, powerful enough batteries, digital remote-control units, and also the miniaturisation of computers, which means that drones can be exceptionally adaptable.

Drones are both affordable and widely available. You just need to make a few decisions when it comes to choosing one, as the types differ significantly. If you are a hobbyist, you could build your own drone, and would undoubtedly find this a fun and rewarding process. However, if money is an object, it would be cheaper to buy one, though some will need some assembling. The size, power and number of rotor blades are also important, as they affect what you can do, how you can fly the drone, and what it will cost.

The types of drones

Picking the best for your needs and budget

Drones are now common enough that there are stores that stock them and, of course, online shops that sell different types. The differences can be as obvious as cost and manufacturer, but more importantly affect how much work you have to do. You're not likely to ever be able to fly a drone home straight from the shop. There are some that need assembling, and some that need their batteries charged first.

RTF

RTF means Ready To Fly. It means that you'll be able to fly it more or less straight out of the box. You will need to charge up the drone's batteries and perhaps put on the rotor blades and bind the drone with the handset. Binding is like the pairing you do with Bluetooth devices. Nonetheless, RTF drones are a good choice for beginners. They can be more expensive, though, as they're aimed at a broader range of users and are capable of doing lots of things.

BNF

This stands for Bind-N-Fly. These drones are sold as complete quadcopters or UAVs, but they don't include the controller. That's the key difference between an RTF and a BNF. You need to buy a separate handset controller, but you might be able to use your old controller. That's not guaranteed but, in theory, you could keep the same controller and use it with different drones. They're not always compatible, but you could easily buy alternative ones.

ARF

This stands for Almost Ready to Fly. You will need to work on the drone before flying. This can mean as little as assembling it, but you might not get a controller or the transmitter/receiver for the drone to be controllable, or the flight control computer that makes flying the drone physically possible. This isn't really aimed at a beginner. You'd choose an ARF drone if you're an existing drone user and already have parts and know how to transfer them to the machine.

Buying your first drone

What to buy and where to get it

You could go on Amazon right now and take your pick from more than 700 different drones. However, you might encounter a problem when it comes to choosing which one to buy, as you will be swamped with jargon and reviews.

Quadcopters cross lines between electronics, hobbyist products and, in some cases, even toys. So, high-street stores that sell any of these could also sell drones. The electronics company Maplin, for example, offers a number of UAVs, but not every store will necessarily have every product. Once you have an idea of the type of drone you want, and the amount of money you can afford to spend on it, use online sites to narrow down your search. Many people buy the first drone they can afford, and don't appreciate there are differences in terms of what each type is useful for.

You also need to look at what type of camera comes with the drone, if any. The cheapest drone not only won't come with a camera, but you also won't be able to fit one to it. Mid and even low-price drones will include basic cameras, but many people will want the same picture quality that you see on YouTube's collection of drone videos. What is often overlooked is getting a drone with a gimbal. This is a mount like a miniature version of the ones used in aerial photography. It offers the camera a wide range of movement, and also enables it to move smoothly. All rotorcraft vibrate, and helicopters have tail rotors specifically to stop the entire machine being flung around in the opposite direction to the main rotors. Gimbals even that out.

UAVs are cheap in the sense that they are quite affordable, but not cheap in the sense that you can't casually keep buying them until you find one that you like. It is a purchase you need to consider carefully.

Decide on the type of drone that would suit your needs, then think about how much you can afford to spend

© David J.Jörgens.mi

Anatomy of a drone

One machine, so very many components

Battery
This is perhaps the most limiting element you'll face. Fully charged ones will typically only power the drone for 20 minutes

Shell
This is the casing; the fuselage of the UAV. Bright colours really help you spot this from a distance

Body
The core of your drone is this hub; all the physical elements connect to this, which is always at the centre of gravity of your UAV

Rotors
These are shaped exactly like aircraft wings, and for the same reason. Their shape affects air flowing over them and that is what produces lift

Landing gear
They let the drone set down on the ground without anything hitting the rotors or body

GPS Aerial
With GPS your drone knows knows exactly where it is, and will make decisions based on that

Booms
The arms of your drone have to be light but strong and thin enough to not get in the way of the rotor's downdraft.

Before you get started

What to buy and where to get it

Ensure it's legal

The laws surrounding drones are constantly changing. One of the most important things to do before you take your drone out is to research and understand the basic laws regarding flying a drone in your country. There are limits to where you can fly, especially near people, airports and military bases, so check before you head out.

Know your boundaries

There's a reason so many stunning drone videos are of landscapes: you cannot fly one within 150 metres of a congested area. Similarly, you cannot fly one within 50 metres of an individual. Also, if you are doing any flying for commercial reasons, you'll need a licence from the Civil Aviation Authority.

5 Essential safety tips

1. Ensure you never fly your drone near people's bodies and faces.

2. Switch off the drone's motor before the controller handset.

3. Remove the rotors when you're not using the UAV.

4. Don't risk flying unless you see weather conditions are good.

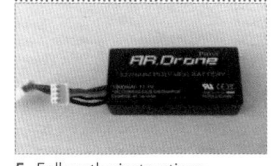

5. Follow the instructions provided for recharging Lithium Polymer batteries.

Pick your spot

The UAV must remain within your sight at all times. If you can't see your drone without binoculars, you're in the wrong. The rule of thumb is that you are limited to 500m (1,640ft) horizontal distance and 400ft altitude. (Note that the Civil Aviation Authority lists altitude in feet, and 400ft is approximately 122m.)

Track the weather

You can't fly a drone in the rain (these are electrical devices you're putting up there), and you must not fly through clouds. Sunshine and rain are easy to spot, but wind speed is harder. Drones vary a lot, but typically if wind is below 28mph (45km/h) then most drones will fly. You'll struggle to get decent video when fighting against strong winds.

Charge your controller

With all the concentration on battery power for the quadcopters themselves, you can forget that your controller actually needs it as well. If your controller fails while your drone is aloft, that drone is going to keep on going until its own battery dies and it falls from the sky. Keeping spare batteries is always a good idea.

Test the camera

Some UAV cameras will just transmit video back to your phone to record there. However, high-end ones stream back so you can see what they're filming, as well as record up to 4K quality video on board. Make sure you have a completely empty SD card, then try and test it to check it's working before you pull off a fantastic aerial flyby that doesn't get recorded.

Watch your time

How long you can keep a drone aloft is limited, due to the limits of battery technology. At present, you can expect to get around of 20 minutes' flying time per charge. Professionals keep it to around ten and carry many spare batteries that they swap in for the rest of the shoot. The best at present are Lithium Polymer (LiPo).

The basics of flying

You're the pilot of an aircraft now

Beat the wind Gusts come from one direction at a time, so if you are buffeted from the right, then you should fly to the right. You'll know when this is necessary, as you'll feel your loss of control. Just also be very aware that your best option may be to land the UAV.

Start small Go out into the garden and place the drone on the ground with the front (where the camera is) facing away from you. Then, start the motor and gently increase the throttle until the UAV rises off the ground. Just take it a few inches off the ground and hold it there.

Hover your drone When your drone is close to the ground, the downdraft from the rotors is reflected up, and makes it hard to keep the UAV steady. Raise it to 1.5m (5ft) and then practise holding it still. This is known as hovering and can be tricky to master.

Crash occasionally It's going to happen, so learn how to get it right by letting the drone crash from a small height. You've got to learn how to quickly recognise when a crash is going to happen, then switch off the throttle straight away.

Know your equipment Check whether your drone comes with auto-levelling controls. If it does, then as soon as you have tilted the UAV in any direction in order to change course or pick up speed, the drone itself will tilt back and get on the level.

Take short hops Practice flying your drone short distances in your garden. You'll be learning the core controls of turning left and right, moving up and down, forward and back. If you do them in short hops, the worst that can happen is that you have to walk over and pick your drone up.

Roll, Pitch, Yaw Tilt your UAV up and down to control the pitch, turn it left and right to control its yaw and wiggle it to control its roll. Pitch the UAV forward and it will go faster because the rotors are pushing it along, but you could also pitch it into the ground if you get it wrong.

Try taking a selfie You are able to buy drones that will lock on to the GPS signal from your phone and basically fly around you like your personal camera crew. However, selfies are great to take because they require precision controls, and they are definitely unique.

Maintaining your machine

Keep your quadcopter flying right

Your drone is subject to enormous stresses. Each of its rotors is really trying to spin the entire machine and, although having four or more of them cancels that out, it strains the airframe. Drones have to be light too, so there are limits to how strong they can be, and to keep it working well, you need to know how to maintain it.

There are two things you should always do: check the batteries and bring spares. Batteries decline in power over time, so get used to having spares when you can and making sure you use them fully. That's harder in a drone than, say, a mobile phone because leaving them on means leaving the device flying. Do what you can, though, and that includes regular cleaning of the contact pads between the battery and the UAV. Bring spares of anything you can. Rotor blades are an essential spare, because you will get through several of those. It's going to be obvious when a blade has broken off in a crash, but they can also develop cracks.

Before you fly, inspect your UAV. Every pilot in the world does a walk-around inspection of their aircraft before flying it; it's considered their responsibility. In your case, you're looking for any damage to the landing gear, or warning LED lights on the flight computer or GPS equipment. You're also looking for any damage to the gimbal mount that holds the camera.

At regular intervals, such as every ten flights or few weeks, open up the drone and clean inside. See if you can rotate the rotors by hand without any difficulty or feel of the blades catching. Then, when your fingers are clear, fire up the motor and listen for any unusual sounds that could reveal wear and tear.

© KMF

Join in with others
There's a whole flying community

Groups are brilliant for offering information on the different types of drones and the best ways to use them. You'll find that there are groups of people online who are interested in very specific machines or uses, such as owners of Phantom products or people who are into shooting location video, or more general groups.

It's definitely worth joining a group, and a good place to try is the Facebook group My First Drone Beginners Group. It's a private-interest group, so it's closed, but you just need to request to join it. You can also use the online groups to find out where there are local flying groups. If there is anything better than hearing from someone about exactly how they use their quadcopter and what problems they've solved, it's seeing them use it in front of you. You'll improve your flying skills, and get entirely new ideas for what you can use drones for.

Perhaps consider entering your drone into competitions. It's about pitching your flying technique against other people and also your brand of quadcopter against others. If you have any competitive spirit, you'll have a blast, but you'll also see useful results. For example, if a Phantom UAV wins every time, you know to take a look at that company's models. There are more organised events in the USA than anywhere else, but you will find that UAVs increasingly feature in more general shows, such as the annual UK Helicopter Show in May. Check for details of the next one on **www.heliukexpo. com/sectors/uav**. Groups are also a first-class source for details about buying and selling UAVs. Members will discuss deals they find, and know where you can get spare parts. Try joining a group and you'll see how you will receive all the practical benefits.

Drone glossary

Essential terms you'll need to master

Accelerometer: Instrument used for measuring acceleration on a given path.

Attitude: This is the orientation of the UAV, whether it's tilting forward or flying upside down.

Autonomous: When a drone is flying by itself on a set path using GPS or other means, rather than actively steered with a controller.

Bind: Connecting a controller to a drone. This is like pairing your phone to an earpiece.

CAA (Civil Aviation Authority): The UK's body in charge of all flight issues and licences. The American equivalent is the FAA, or Federal Aviation Authority.

Controller: The device you use to fly the UAV. They can be exactly the same as old-style helicopter remote controls, or you can use apps on a phone.

Downdraft: The force of the wind from the rotor blades

when they're spinning. It's partly that which gives lift, partly the shape of the blades and how the air flows over them.

FPV (first-person view): A way of controlling your drone which lets you see what the drone is seeing in the air in real-time.

Gimbal: The type of mount that lets a camera stay steady on a UAV while turning and when in high winds.

GPS: The same as the global positioning system used in your satnav, but here how certain drones can know and record their position.

Gyroscope: You could not fly your UAV straight and steady if it didn't include a gyroscope that detects when it's level.

Lithium Polymer or LiPo: Currently the best batteries for drones due to their great power given their relatively small size.

Multirotor: A term for a drone with several rotor blades.

Payload: Anything a UAV is carrying that isn't needed for flight, usually a camera.

Pitch: Together with roll and yaw, this is a description of the UAV's movement in flight. Pitch is when it is tilted up or down.

Quadcopter: A four-bladed drone, the most common basic type, because that number of blades gives more stability.

Roll: Together with pitch and yaw, this is a description of the UAV's movement in flight. Roll is when you wiggle the drone as if you intend to twist it all the way around its central axis.

UAV (unmanned aerial vehicle): This covers all drones and is what the Civil Aviation Authority calls them.

Yaw: TYaw is when the drone is turning slightly left or right.

4K Video: The best drones have cameras that shoot video at 4K resolution. They tend to stream 1K video in flight so that you see what you're filming.

Top 5 drones

For fun with the family to aerial photography, drones are not only incredibly versatile but also surprisingly affordable

As technology advances and prices fall, the demand for consumer drones continues to grow. Drones are available in all shapes and sizes from the tiny, entry-level Blade Nano QX to the high-end, professional Turbo Ace Matrix.

It can all be a bit confusing, as these remote control or autonomous aircraft go by a variety of names, including UAVs, drones and quadcopters. These are largely interchangeable, although the term quadcopter refers to the number of rotors. From as little as £40/$60, you can experience the fun and excitement of owning a drone without breaking the bank. Explore, perform stunts, and even play multiplayer games. You can choose from a range of drones to suit your budget and experience level. With so many drones on the market, it can be hard to find the right one. We have compiled a guide to introduce you five of the coolest drones on the market, which will suit everyone from first-timers to filmmakers. Whether you are a complete beginner and want to learn how to fly or an expert pilot looking for a high-end camera drone to take photos and record video, we've got you covered.

HUBSAN X4 H107 Quadcopter

Easy to use and good for stunts, the X4 is inexpensive and suitable for beginners

Small enough to fit in the palm of your hand, the X4 is one of the most compact drones on the market. This not only makes the X4 safer to use indoors and more suitable for less experienced users, but it also means it's fast and agile enough to perform a range of tricks and stunts.

With four motors and a six-axis flight control system, the X4 quadcopter is stable and easy to operate. A remote control transmitter allows you to fly the X4 remotely from a distance of up to 100 metres. The rechargeable 240mAh battery provides around ten minutes of flight time.

Hubsan offer two models of the X4 in the forms of the H107L and H107C. The main difference between them is the addition of a 2 megapixel HD camera mounted on the H107C, allowing you take pictures and record video from on-board the drone.

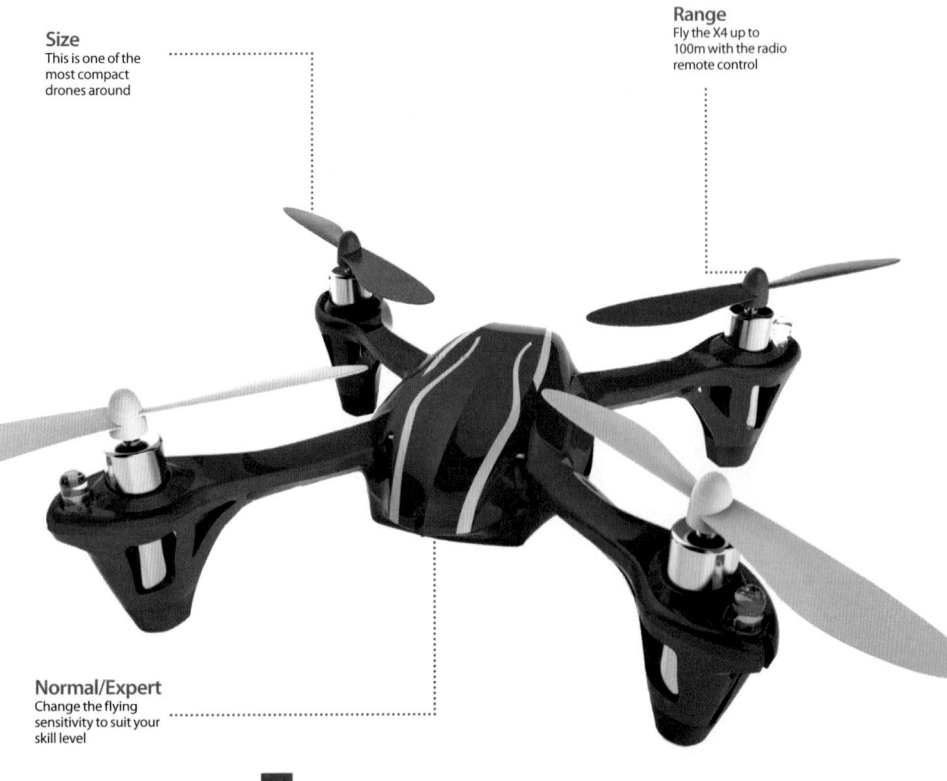

Size
This is one of the most compact drones around

Range
Fly the X4 up to 100m with the radio remote control

Normal/Expert
Change the flying sensitivity to suit your skill level

Utilise different modes

You can adjust the difficulty of flying the X4 by selecting one of two flight modes: Normal or Expert. Normal mode allows novice pilots to get to grips with the basics of flying, while the Expert mode lets you attempt more difficult and complex manoeuvres.

This makes it a suitable drone for beginners and users looking to gain flying experience. Start with Normal mode selected and as you become more adept at flying, you can progress to the Expert mode and develop your skills further.

In Expert mode, the X4 can fly in excess of 25mph and perform a range of cool tricks including turning cycles, banking and even figure of eights. One of the more impressive stunts you can perform is a flip. By pulling the stick on the remote control in one direction and then quickly in the opposite direction, the drone will flip over in an impressive manner. Aerobatics, however, should only be attempted in large spaces or outdoors to reduce the risk of any damage or injury.

Since you will likely be using it for stunts, you may also want to consider investing in the Hubsan X4 Quadcopter Crash Pack that provides extra rotor blades, a spare battery and propeller guards. Priced at around £45/$55, the X4 mini quadcopter is cheap, lots of fun and an ideal first drone for beginners. Catering to all experience levels, its Normal and Expert modes are useful for helping you to improve your flying skills.

Use it for...

- **Fun** This compact drone caters to beginners and experts, so it's great to play around with.

- **Races** Its weight and size make it fast and agile, so a good contender for races.

- **Stunts** The Expert mode is perfect for stunts, and you can do anything from banking to figures of eight.

- **Games** With its versatility, compact size, price and level of experience, it's perfect for messing around.

"By pulling the stick on the remote control in one direction and then quickly in the opposite direction, the drone will flip over in an impressive manner"

Top features

The X4 is light and compact, making it very fast and agile during flight.

You can choose between Normal and Expert modes to adjust the flying sensitivity.

Its low cost makes it suitable for beginners learning to fly, but it also caters to experienced users.

All images ©Hubsan

3DR Solo

3DR has worked with GoPro to create a smart, capable and easy-to-fly camera drone

Top features

Smart Shots provide you with a range of preset camera angles.

The videogame-themed remote control makes flying a much more familiar experience.

Choose from a range of compatible GoPros to mount to the Solo.

3D Robotics, the company behind the upcoming Solo quadcopter, claims this is the world's smartest drone. Mount your own compatible GoPro camera onto the Solo to create an incredibly flexible and versatile camera drone.

Two powerful computers housed in the main body and the controller means the Solo can offer a number of advanced features, such as Smart Shots and the Pixhawk 2 autopilot. The Smart Shots technology allows you to capture footage using a range of camera set-pieces, which the Solo automatically performs, including Cable Cam, Orbit and Selfie. Cable Cam, for example, will lock the drone onto a virtual cable between two waypoints, allowing you to freely control the camera and record the perfect footage.

You can further enhance the camera stability by investing in the additional solo gimbal, which helps the GoPro to achieve even smoother video footage. The Solo comes with an innovative remote control, designed to look and feel like a videogame controller. It adds familiarity and removes the learning-curve associated with

Use it for...

- **Videos** Use your own GoPro of the built-in camera, and try Smart Shots for a range of options.

- **Exploration** Use a live feed and the autopilot function to wander off to unexplored places.

- **Photography** You can use the preset Selfie mode for a truly unique portrait of yourself.

- **Sports** The Solo's remote control is reminiscient of a videogame controller for fun races.

"You can further enhance the camera stability by investing in the additional solo gimbal, which helps the GoPro to achieve even smoother video footage"

Speeds
The quadcopter is
capable of reaching
speeds of 55mph

Smart drone
Two powerful
computers makes this
drone very smart indeed

Compatibility
The Solo is compatible
with a whole range of
different GoPros

using typical drone controllers. True to the videogame theme, it even features a dedicated pause button, which activates the air brake and stops the Solo mid-flight. In addition, one-button flight controls allow you to take off, land and return home without any user input. These autopilot functions mean the Solo is easier to use, regardless of your flying experience.

Extend the functionality

As well as flying the Solo from the bespoke remote control, you can dock your phone or tablet onto the controller and download the free app for iOS and Android devices to access even more functionality. From the app you can access the GoPro's camera controls as well as viewing a live HD feed, allowing you to fly the drone in first-person view (FPV).

The four, ten-inch diameter propellers and large 5,200mAh battery provides the Solo with a maximum speed of 55mph and a flight time of 20 to 25 minutes, depending on the payload and weather conditions. With a range of over half a mile, it's capable of capturing both high-speed and long-distance video. LED spotlighting helps you track the drone and makes using it in low-light conditions easier. Best suited to users with some flying experience, you'll have to dig deep as the Solo will set you back around £980/$1,000.

Parrot Bebop 2 drone

The Bebop 2 is a faster, longer-lasting drone that could be the ultimate flying machine

The Parrot Bebop 2 builds on the success of the original consumer camera drone by featuring a more durable body, higher quality camera and longer flight time. The Bebop 2 is one of the most advanced drones you can buy, and is absolutely packed with gadgets and technology. The ultrasound and pressure sensors measure its altitude while the three-axis gyroscope and accelerometer keep the drone stable in flight. Keeping all this tech safe is the new and improved glass reinforced chassis and shockproof feet. Weighing just 500 grams, the lightweight and compact design makes the Bebop 2 surprisingly portable.

Four brushless outrunner engines provide enough power for the Bebop 2 to reach speeds of up to 37mph horizontally and 13mph vertically. It can reach its top speed in just 14 seconds, allowing it to climb to 328 feet in less than 20 seconds. It's incredibly fast and thanks to its rechargeable 2700mAh battery, has an impressive flight time of 25 minutes.

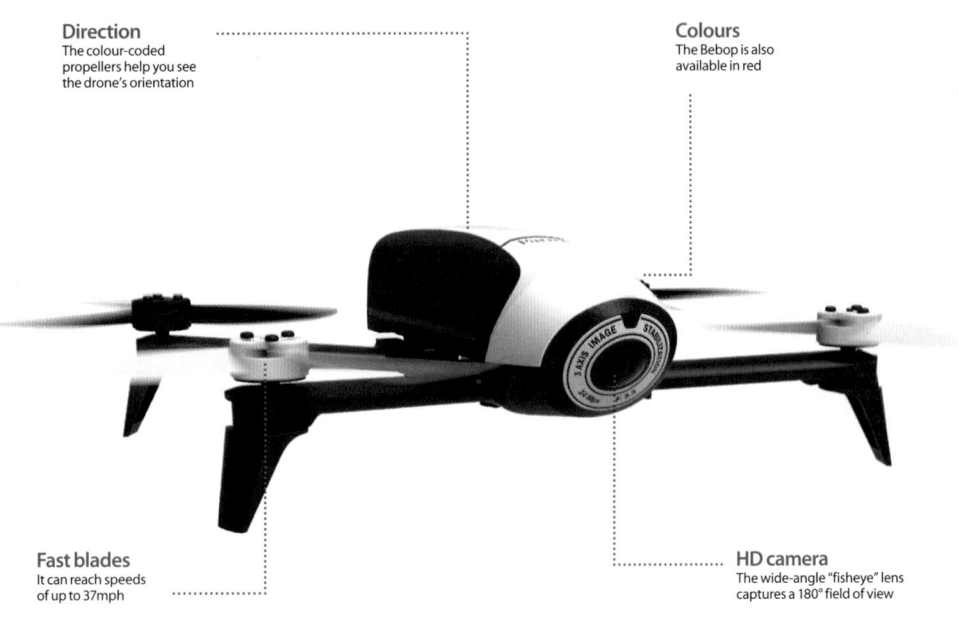

Direction
The colour-coded propellers help you see the drone's orientation

Colours
The Bebop is also available in red

Fast blades
It can reach speeds of up to 37mph

HD camera
The wide-angle "fisheye" lens captures a 180° field of view

Flying action camera

One of the key selling points of the drone is its ability to take pictures and record high-definition video using the 14-megapixel on-board camera. The front-facing camera has a fish-eye lens and has been specifically designed to produce stabilised, wide-angle shots. Images are live streamed to your piloting device and saved on to the 8GB flash memory drive which can be easily transferred onto your phone, tablet or computer.

Flying the Bebop 2 is easy with the FreeFlight 3 app available for iOS or Android smartphones and tablets. A powerful on-board computer with a dual-core processor and fast Wi-Fi ensures all the data from the seven sensors is instantly relayed back to you through the app, ensuring you remain in complete control. If you prefer to fly by eye, you can use the LED lights on the back of the drone to help you see which direction it's facing.

Interested in taking your flying to the next level? You can invest in the optional Parrot Skycontroller Black Edition remote control. The two-handed controller features dual-joysticks for unparalled control as well as a Wi-Fi extender which increases the range up to nearly 2km. The Android-powered Skycontroller works with the FreeFlight 3 piloting app which means you can connect it directly to the Bebop 2 without needing a smartphone or tablet.

Available from early 2016, the Bebop drone will retail for around £439.99 / $499.99.

Use it for...

- **Photography** The 14-megapixel on-board camera is the highlight of this amazing drone.

- **Videos** You can keep producing stabilised shots without filling up the 8GB memory drive.

- **Exploration** By upgrading to the Black Edition remote control your range extends to 2km.

- **Fun** Its incredible speeds of up to 37mph and an impressive battery life makes for endless playtime.

"Flying the Bebop 2 is easy with the FreeFlight 3 app available for iOS or Android smartphones and tablets."

Top features

The 14-megapixel HD camera is digitally stabilised on three-axis using powerful computer algorithms.

The engines and propellers have emergency cut-out features in case of contact or damage.

The Bebop 2 easily connects to your Android or iOS smartphone or tablet using Wi-Fi MIMO (2.4Ghz and 5Ghz).

All images ©Parrot

Parrot AR.Drone 2.0

The AR.Drone 2.0 is lots of fun, offering an HD camera and multiplayer gaming potential

Now in its second generation, the AR.Drone 2.0 is smaller, lighter and more agile than its predecessor and available in a range of colours. Compared with the more expensive Parrot Bebop, the AR.Drone 2 is considered an entry-level drone. It offers a built-in HD camera optimised for video recording and can be piloted in real-time from the AR.FreeFlight app. The app is available to download for free on iOS or Android devices and allows you to fly, record videos and much more.

Included with the drone are indoor and outdoor hulls. They are designed to protect it in different environments, for example the indoor hull adds propeller guards. Weighing just 380g with the outdoor hull attached, four motors drive the drone up to speeds of nearly 25mph. The 1,000mAh battery provides approximately 15 minutes of flight time. A host of on-board sensors from gyroscopes to accelerometers ensure the drone is stable and easy to fly. You can control the drone in first person view (FPV) from the front camera's live feed on your paired device. The built-in camera features a 92°

Use it for...

- **Videos** The built-in camera records great HD video, so start filming straight away!

- **Battles** Don't bash your drones together just yet – race your drones via an iOS game on your phone!

- **Multiplayer** Use your drone to play games with others on your phone to share the drone experience.

- **Exploration** The outdoor hull protects your drone, so you can take it anywhere!

"From adjusting the speed in real-time to programming the drone to move in a certain way, you can create impressive-looking travelling, pan and crane shots"

Top features

Easily take pictures and record HD video thanks to the AR.Drone 2.0's built-in camera.

Choose between indoor and outdoor hulls to protect your precious drone.

You can play games like AR.Race and AR.Pursuit with friends and family on your phone.

Speed
The quadcopter is
capable of reaching
speeds of 55mph

Sensors
Sensors ensure the
drone is stable and
easy to fly

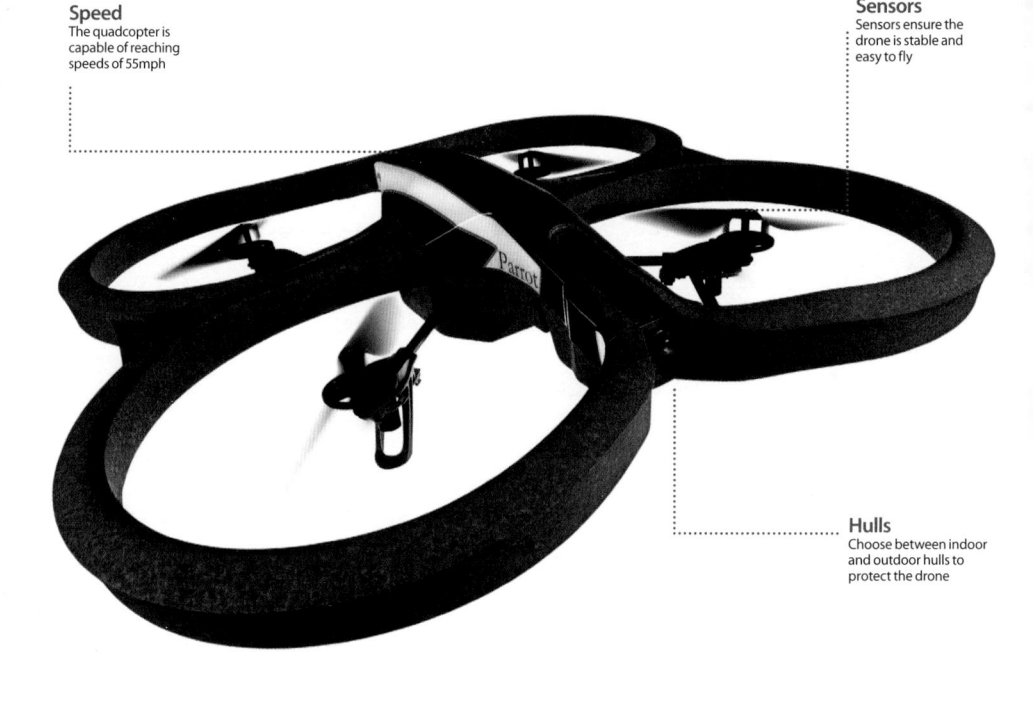

Hulls
Choose between indoor
and outdoor hulls to
protect the drone

wide-angle lens and is capable of recording HD video. Digital stabilisation and software processing help create smooth and stable shots. You can save videos on the fly directly to your smartphone or tablet over Wi-Fi and even upload your movies to YouTube directly from the app.

Access "Director Mode" from the app to create high quality and professional-looking video. From adjusting the speed in real-time to programming the drone to move in a certain way, you can create impressive-looking travelling, pan and crane shots.

Multiplayer gaming

The front camera has another use too: it can detect the hull colour of other AR.Drone's, which makes multiplayer gaming possible. Currently only available on iOS devices, the objective of games such as AR.Pursuit is to earn points by taking turns attacking and fleeing from your opponent's drone. Multiplayer games require two sets of drones and iOS devices, but getting friends or family involved is great fun.

The AR.Drone 2.0 is priced at £249/$299 for the Elite edition, or a little more for the Power edition. There is no functional difference between them, the models simply refer to what accessories are bundled, as well the inclusion of a larger 1,500mAh battery for the Power edition.

DJI Phantom

The phantom range from dji come packed with incredible features for all users

The DJI Phantom 3 is the first drone in the successful Phantom series to feature a built-in camera. Historically, they have been considered high-end or 'prosumer' drones that required a separate camera to be mounted onto the body. Its predecessor, the Vision+ brought silky smooth and professional-looking aerial video to the mainstream market, and the Phantom 3 expands these capabilities further. Two versions of the Phantom 3 are available; the Advanced model features a 12 megapixel camera capable of recording video at 60 frames per second in Full HD resolution. The more expensive Professional model can record video up to 4K at 30 frames per second. Paired with a three-axis gimbal, both offer exceptional stability for a consumer drone and empower you to capture professional-grade video and imagery. Similar in design to previous models, the white plastic body is relatively portable considering the inclusion of a camera and gimbal, weighing in at 1.28kg. Powered by a 4,480mAh battery, the four rotors are capable of propelling the Phantom 3 up to 35mph for approximately 23

Attractive design
The Phantom range is hugely popular among many hobbyists

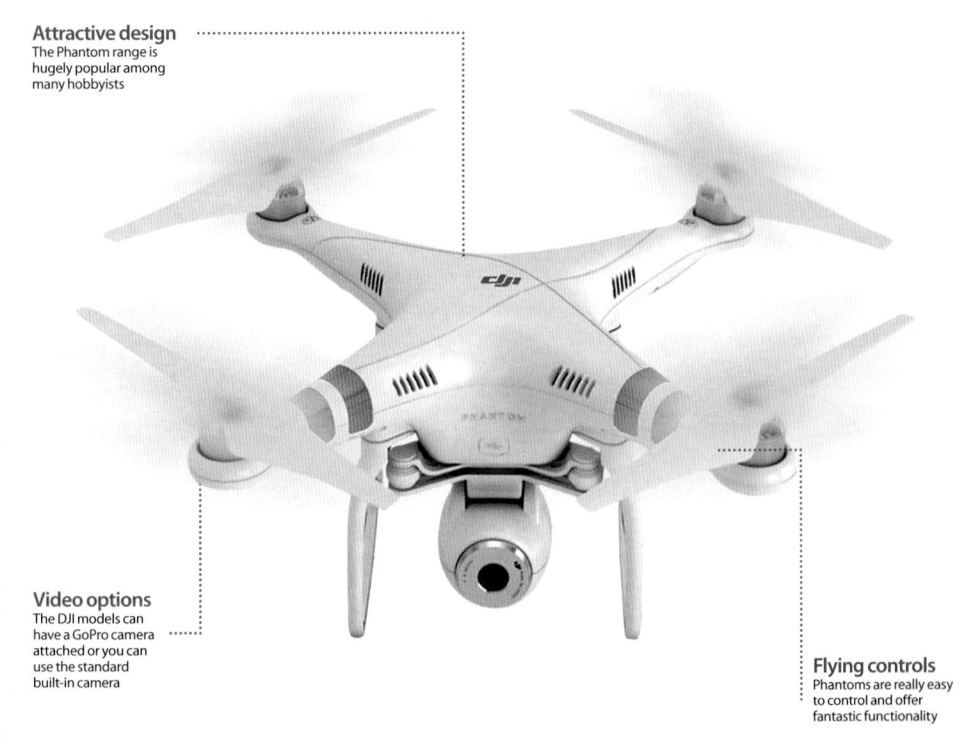

Video options
The DJI models can have a GoPro camera attached or you can use the standard built-in camera

Flying controls
Phantoms are really easy to control and offer fantastic functionality

minutes of flight time. Download the free DJI Pilot app on your Android or iOS device to access Live HD View, flight settings, remote photo and video control, as well as the Director video editor. The Live HD View feature beams an HD camera feed, in real-time, to your connected phone or tablet. Utilising DJI's Lightbridge technology, it enables you to view and control the drone up to an incredible distance of 1.2 miles or 1.9 kilometres.

Complete control

Precise flight and camera control of the Phantom 3 is achievable using the included remote control. With your connected phone or tablet placed in the dock of the controller, the two physical thumb sticks allow you to stay in complete control of the drone. In addition to manual control, you can set waypoints, specific altitudes and even order the drone to return home.

It is priced at £899/$999 and £1,159/$1,259 for the Advanced and Professional models, respectively. The Phantom 3 is positioned at the top of the mainstream camera drone market and is therefore best suited for users with some experience. However, a Beginner mode assists first-time pilots learning to fly by limiting the maximum distance and altitude the drone can reach. Alongside the previous Phantoms, this third iteration is likely to take the drone world by storm.

Use it for...

- **Video** At the top of the mainstream market, this drone offers great stability for steady pans and shots.

- **Exploration** With the Live View you can see locations that would otherwise be hard or risky to reach.

- **Photography** With the option to shoot with the built-in camera or a GoPro, great photos are a must!

- **Work** In this price range, the Phantom is aimed at professionals, and are highly powerful.

"Utilising DJI's Lightbridge technology, it enables you to view and control the drone up to an incredible distance of 1.2 miles or 1.9 kilometres"

Top features

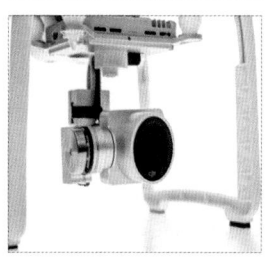

You can dock your phone or tablet into the remote controller for precision flying.

The Phantom range is a top choice if you want to shoot videos or take photos.

Live View provides you with a real-time HD video feed up to 1.2 miles away.

Getting started with FPV

Turn your drone into the ultimate eye in the sky and upgrade to first-person view when flying

First-person view, or FPV, means you see what your drone sees through its camera or attached GoPro. Instead of just squinting up at your quadcopter from the ground, you can see the live view through the on-board camera, using special goggles or a portable monitor, or in some cases an Android or iOS mobile device. This lets you fly further, higher and faster without getting too disorientated or confused.

Watching from the ground, it's all too easy to lose track of which way your drone is facing and whether you need to reverse the stick inputs to make it turn the right way. When you're flying FPV, left and right never get reversed, because your perspective is the same as your drone's. Flying FPV is also a lot more immersive. You don't need to wait until you land to see the aerial footage; you can experience it as you fly. Nothing is worse than wasting your entire battery on trying to get the perfect shot of a view or a building, just to find out later your were pointing your drone the wrong way. This doesn't just help frame shots for aerial photography, it makes a whole new kind of flying possible – quadcopter racing.

"When you're flying FPV, left and right never get reversed, because your perspective is the same as your drone's"

Digital vs analogue

Many ready-to-fly UAVs, like the Parrot BeBop and DJI Phantom 2 Vision series, provide high-quality video downlinks that you can watch through an app on your phone or tablet. These use Wi-Fi to transmit the video signal, which requires a special antenna on the control transmitter to be able to reach further than a few tens of metres. But more importantly, Wi-Fi signals experience a slight latency, or lag, in the image that you see on the screen. For framing a shot, or flying fairly sedately, this isn't a problem but for high-speed, low-level flying, especially around obstacles such as buildings and trees, Wi-Fi video isn't responsive enough. That isn't a problem for home-built multirotors though, because these almost always use analogue video systems. The picture is sent as a much lower resolution analogue TV signal over 5.8GHz radio frequencies. Although these systems can suffer from 'snow' interference and the picture quality is generally worse, it updates virtually instantly. This is ideal for acrobatic flying. Analogue systems are also much cheaper and easier to install yourself.

"The picture is sent as a much lower resolution analogue TV signal over 5.8GHz radio frequencies"

Mount the headset
Mounting the headset on a tripod as an external monitor lets you quickly glance up for take off and landing

Pointing the video antenna downwards can improve your reception but you need long enough landing legs to avoid squashing it

Below View from inside The Quanum

The view through FPV goggles is always much lower resolution than the HD video your drone records

The FPV display shows you some vital information, allowing you to pilot your drone safely and easily

© M Alford,

Be careful of wire fences and power lines – they are very hard to see in FPV goggles

From this height, your drone might just be a speck in the sky, but FPV lets you stay in full control

Connecting it up

If you have a simple mini quad, like the one we showed you how to build elsewhere in the book, you can upgrade it for FPV flying for under £110. The Mobius ActionCam can output analogue TV video at the same time as recording its own HD digital video on the memory card. This lets you save weight and money by combining two cameras in one. If you're already flying with a GoPro camera, it's better to add a simple front-facing 600TVL (TV lines) board camera, such as the CC1333-B (£23 from www.hobbyrc.co.uk).

Whichever camera you use, you will need to connect it to a video transmitter (VTX). We used the 200 milliwatt Aomway mini transmitter, which has plenty of range for park flying. If you need to make up your own cable to connect the two, you can quite easily hack an old mini-USB cable. Ignore the white wire inside the cable, which you don't need because it is the audio signal, and simply connect the yellow wire to the video-in pin on the transmitter, red to +5V and black to ground.

To catch the video signal at the other end, you need a 5.8GHz receiver. FPV goggles such as the FatShark range have a receiver built-in but these goggles cost £200-£300. Until you know for sure that FPV flying is for you, it's better to start with a separate video receiver, such as the £23 Boscam RX305. This will plug into any

Make sure you stay well clear of people and buildings. FPV doesn't make you crash-proof!

analogue screen and the best one for beginners is the Quanum DIY. This £34 kit includes a 4.3-inch screen with a simple lens and case. You can wear it like a bulky pair of goggles, or you can take the lens out and use it as a monitor with a sunshade. Your first few flights in FPV can feel quite claustrophobic, particularly during takeoff and landing. Using the Quanum DIY as a monitor to begin with will make the learning process much more comfortable. If you are prone to motion sickness, flying FPV with goggles can also make you feel nauseous at first. Watching the action on a monitor screen, where you still have your peripheral vision to orient yourself, will definitely help. If you later decide to upgrade to FatShark goggles, your Quanum screen won't be wasted because you can use it to allow a 'passenger' to fly along with you, sharing the same view.

Flying further

Once you have installed and tested this basic setup, there are some easy upgrades to greatly improve the experience of flying your drone in this manner. The most important one is an antenna upgrade. The basic stick antennas supplied with the transmitter and receiver only provide good reception when they are aligned parallel to each other.

As the quadcopter banks and pitches, its antenna will inevitably tilt out of alignment and your reception will suffer. Simply by replacing both antennas with 'cloverleaf' circularly polarised antennas (only £10 for two), you will hugely improve your effective range for FPV. This is actually a much better way to improve your range than increasing the power of the transmitter on the quadcopter.

The tyranny of the inverse-square law means that doubling the transmitting power only improves your range by about 40 per cent, whereas by switching to the cloverleaf antennas you can double your range without using any more extra power.

Take care
You are completely blind with the goggles on, which comes with its own range of dangers and issues

FPV AND THE LAW

In the UK, the Civil Aviation Authority requires that small unmanned aircraft, such as quadcopters, can only be flown when the operator has 'direct, unaided visual contact' with the aircraft. This means that even using FPV, it is illegal to fly so high or far away that you can't see it from the ground.

Head-up display

A more advanced upgrade is to add an on-screen display (OSD). This takes telemetry from the drone's flight controller and displays it as text and numbers overlaid over your view through the camera. You can configure what information is displayed on the OSD, from something as simple as just the battery voltage to an entire dashboards' worth of data, including speed, altitude, heading and artificial horizon. If your quadcopter has a GPS unit fitted, your OSD can also show how far you have travelled and an arrow pointing back to the launch point. This provides a very handy reference point – from 100 metres up, one field looks very much like another! A very popular OSD unit is the £16 Micro MinimOSD. This postage-stamp-sized circuit board plugs into the serial port pins in the centre of the Naze32 flight controller, as well as the video connectors on both the camera and the VTX. The extra data is only added to the transmitted video feed, so the aerial footage that you record on your Mobius or GoPro remains pristine.

Whether you decide to stick with a budget system or to upgrade as far as current technology will allow, flying FPV is a breathtaking experience and definitely something that every drone pilot should try at least once. It isn't just the closest thing to flying a plane; it's the closest thing to being a bird.

> "It isn't just the closest thing to flying a plane; it's the closest thing to being a bird"

Use the Parrot Skycontroller to pilot your Bebop in style

You can always see what
your drone sees thanks to the
monitor you can attach to your
Phantom's controller

Extreme filming
A drone camera films Andy Lewis on a slackline between buildings in central Bangkok

40

Photographing & filming

How to create professional looking aerial shots and movies without a big budget drone

Drone filming is big news on television right now. Almost every time you sit down to watch the news, there will be some great sequences showing buildings and places in a way we've never seen before, from angles that show us exactly what we need to see, but would be impossible to shoot without the help of a stable drone. Many of us would love to try our hand at drone photography and filming, whether it's just for entertainment or for business and professional purposes, but don't know where to begin. So here's our guide to getting started, along with some tips on what to watch for and how to avoid the pitfalls. While you may have mastered flying your drone, this takes everything one step further, and requires a lot of precision.

> "While you may have mastered flying your drone, this takes everything one step further, and requires a lot of precision"

©Corbis

41

Choosing a suitable drone for photos and filming

Drone and camera technology is advancing all the time. There's nothing more frustrating than spending money on a quadcopter and camera that just a few weeks later is replaced by a better model. But quadcopter technology at a price point that's affordable has now matured into a stable platform that is very reliable. However, video camera technology is still advancing and improving, so it's important to choose a drone with a useful life ahead of it. Our recommendation for a suitable filming UAV is to choose one that allows you to change the camera and the gimbal.

The DJI Phantom is designed to lift the GoPro series of cameras. In just a short time, GoPro has become the go-to brand for small, high-technology cameras, now recording up to 4K in video and burst rate stills of over 12 frames per second. But as the GoPro capability increases, the camera size amazingly doesn't change, making your UAV easily upgradable.

Secondly, the gimbals are steadily improving, with the Zenmuse gimbal currently the leader in stability. This can also be upgraded on certain Phantom models, so you're buying into a full upgradable platform that can grow with you as advancements roll out and your skills develop. For example, at its release. DJI has a camera that it claims is better than a GoPro, although after that statement GoPro launched the Hero4 Session. It's a never-ending, Darwinian game of leapfrog, and you're just going to have to keep up!

A fairly typical scene, but one that can be vastly improved with some creative filming

"Our recommendation for a suitable filming UAV is choose one that allows you to change the camera and the gimbal"

Learning to fly for photography and film making

Our number one rule for creating great films from a UAV is really simple: stop thinking about it as a drone and simply think of it as a rock-solid camera without a tripod that can be placed at almost any point of your choosing and moved as if by an invisible hand. At first, there will be some novelty value in seeing your footage from an elevated view yet, while this is a great feature, it soon wears off. Begin thinking about composition and planning shots from all angles and your skills will quickly move forwards. UAVs can create great looking film footage even at ground level. Their ability to move in between objects and across scenery as if being operated by the smoothest walking cameraman ever is

what makes them so good. So don't just think about high viewpoints, look at how you can fly your drone camera in between archways and trees to create great looking films.

If you only want to shoot still photographs it's a relatively straightforward skill to learn. Once you've mastered your quadcopter flying skills, it's simply a matter of achieving a composition that you're happy with and hitting the shutter button. Remember though, that a good drone pilot does not necessarily make a good photographer, let alone a great filmmaker. Practise photography and read up on basic skills first. But by just taking still photographs, you're missing out on the coolest, most creative part of aerial filming – shooting those great, super smooth camera moves. Here's how you get started.

"Once you're proficient with simple tracking shots, try setting your drone into a hover somewhere and then practise panning and tilting"

Filming high speed action shots is now entirely possible without the need to hire a helicopter

Aerial shots like this are interesting and dynamic

© Rizikianos / Dronestagram

How to create those super cool Hollywood camera moves

Chances are that if you're new to flying a quadcopter, you're loving zooming and diving around your patch of sky like a swallow chasing insects. But to create those professional looking aerial drone shots, the mantra is 'less is more'. Get used to the idea that your UAV movement needs to be a gentle one and that your camera gimbal moves need to be the same; slow and gentle. Start off by practising a simple move past an object such as a car or a building, with the camera set at an angle of 45 degrees to the subject. Don't even move the camera gimbal, simply roll the camera, then gently 'walk' your drone past the object, so that it appears in shot, then steadily moves out of shot as you pass it by.

Try this on a large building or something with several objects, such as a row of parked cars. Play it back and just look at how cool such a simple technique can be on camera with a little practice. You see? Less is more. This is called a tracking shot. Now to add in some camera moves.

Once you're proficient with simple tracking shots, set your drone into a hover somewhere and practise panning and tilting. Panning is swivelling the camera horizontally, just as you would if turning your head to follow a passing car. The drone stays still, the gimbal moves the camera. Pans can be different speeds, from gentle moves as if you were admiring a beautiful landscape right through to 'whip pans' which is the type of camera move you'll see in motorsport when a high speed car flashes past a camera at close range. Try to experiment with different speeds of panning and you'll see that smooth, gentle pans work best with UAVs. Now try a tilt. Tilt is taking the camera pointing at the horizon and slowly rotating it downwards, just as you would if you walked to a cliff edge and looked over it. Tilts can start looking out horizontally then smoothly look down. Or you can start looking vertically downwards, before tilting upwards to show the subject. This second shot is called a 'reveal' and is the type of move that the Hollywood camera operators use all the time. But you can do the same thing with your drone. Once you've practised these moves, it's time to bring everything together with combinations of UAV tracking movements with gimbal pans and tilts to create rock solid camera moves that you'd think had been shot from a helicopter. The best way to film a sequence like that is to have a pre-planned idea in your head of what you want the finished sequence to look like. Combining these movements takes practice, but planning in your head where you're going to fly your drone, when you're going to move the camera gimbal and where you plan to end can result in some great looking footage.

Once you're confident with combining drone and camera gimbal moves, it's time to move on to things like 'reveals' and using what is known as the parallax effect. As we mentioned, a 'reveal' shot is one that steadily brings into view the main subject. You're starting with a simple scene, then adding the subject and 'revealing' it to the viewer. Some great reveals include running your UAV across an open field, before lifting up your drone and tilting to reveal a magnificent castle. Finally, one of the trickiest shots to get right is a parallax move. This manoeuvre requires two objects, one in the foreground and one in the background. Fly your UAV past the closest object to reveal the second subject behind it. You'll see that the addition of the foreground subject adds drama to the shot and makes it look like your drone camera is moving much further than it actually is. Wildlife and nature cameramen use this to reveal one mountain from behind another. When you're not flying your camera UAV, a good way to practise is to sit and study television programmes. Drone sequences are frequently used, so watch for them and then try and reverse engineer the shot to work out how it was done and think of locations and situations where you can use those techniques yourself. Filming using drones is an addictive thing and you'll quickly find yourself mentally planning moves everywhere you go, much to the annoyance of your friends and family.

Above all, don't be disheartened if you don't nail the shot right away. It takes professional production companies several 'takes' to get a shot absolutely right, so be prepared to practise and practise some more. The first time you nail a great aerial camera move, you'll feel a huge smile coming on as you see what you've achieved. Next

Develop a story behind your aerial shooting by planning ahead

time you're watching TV, look out for tracking, tilts, pans and reveals in camera moves. You'll see them employed in every programme you watch – they are the basic tools of any cameraman's trade.

One final thing about filming; don't forget to 'pre-roll' the camera for around five seconds before you start your move, then hold position for another five seconds with the camera still rolling at the end. This gives what editors call 'headroom'. It's that little bit of wiggle room to shuffle a sequence around when editing. Make sure you do this, you'll thank yourself for it later.

Practise your skills and study
Great aerial filming takes research, practice and patience

Reverse engineer aerial sequences that you see on television and at the cinema. Watch some of the great aerial camera moves in blockbuster movies, documentaries and other productions, then try to work out how they were achieved. For sure, the subject material may be way more spectacular than your own,

but the same principles apply. You really need to start thinking like an aerial cameraman and study not just drone footage, but helicopter-based gyro-stabilised work shot on high-end Cineflex systems. The budget may be bigger and the equipment more expensive, but the same techniques also apply to your UAV.

Organising your edit

Learning how to edit can be daunting, so it pays to be organised

It's vital to be able to edit your hard earned footage, or at least have a friend who can. Being organised is a major help in managing and editing your material. Start by downloading your clips into a separate project folder. Don't just download everything into your computer's default photo or video folder. Create a separate folder for the project and name everything there. After this, your editing software will have everything to hand. Once you're finished, your project can easily be archived to an external hard drive, but if you decide to change something in your edit, everything is still in place and your video editing software will be able to access your clips.

It's all in the edit

Once you return home with your footage, the work really starts. How do you edit the footage into something that's coherent and actually good to watch? We don't have space here for a tutorial on film editing, but there are some techniques to editing aerial footage that are worth considering, especially if you're starting out learning how to edit your drone footage for the first time.

Rule number one: what's the story? You don't need a script or a team of people behind you to create a short film with your drone that tells a story. It doesn't even need to have actors or action sequences. Your drone can take the viewer on a journey through a scene and reveal the subject in ways they've never seen before. Hopefully, as you were shooting you were beginning to see a sequence appearing that you might like to put together that will work well and flow smoothly, while holding your viewer's attention. What about sound? The whine of your quadcopter motors just isn't going to cut it. Good sound is easily 50 per cent of a quality aerial sequence. Decide on sound before you start the edit. There are a great many sources of royalty free music, with Vimeo having a good library of free music or very low licence fees. Finding the right soundtrack takes time, but it's worth the effort to find music that fits the pace and context of your film. Stay away from cheesy rock music sound tracks, YouTube is littered with them.

> "Finding the right soundtrack takes time, but it's worth the effort to find music that fits the pace and context of your film"

Once you have your music chosen, lay it down on your editing software's timeline and listen to it. Listen for a beat and transitions in the music. Those are the points at which your shots will transition from one to another – on the beat. Your viewers will appreciate being taken on an aerial journey like this when your footage flows with the music. The trick with editing aerial footage is to make your clips fit the beat of the music, not vice versa. Choose a length of only around two minutes and edit your soundtrack to this length. Then start fitting your clips around that. Remember when we talked about pre-rolling the camera before you start a move? Now you'll be glad you did that, as you have excess to trim off and make your job easy. Even so, you'll be surprised at how much footage is needed to hold your viewer's attention even for this short time.

As you progress and become better at UAV filming, you'll start to plan things more, including having a shot list noted down of sequences that you want to film. This will dramatically reduce the amount of excess footage you have left over, plus it will mean your edit is far, far quicker because you already know what you're going to do when you sit down to create your film.

Once you're done, export your movie and upload it to your online account. As well as YouTube, Vimeo is a great free platform for displaying your work, plus it has a community of enthusiastic and creative people who often leave useful comments to help you. Just like learning to fly your drone, aerial filming takes practice. But persevere with it and you'll quickly become accomplished and justifiably proud of your work as you strive to even greater things. It's extremely addictive and very, very satisfying.

Best kit to use

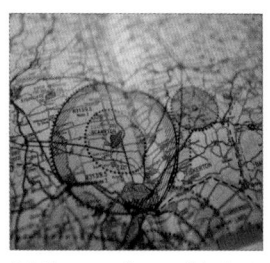

Aviation maps Responsible drone flying is knowing where to avoid. Study an aviation map and be aware of prohibited zones.

Gimbals DJI offers a variety of gimbals to be used with different cameras, so drones can use other cameras as technology advances.

Memory and storage You'll need lots of storage for your footage. Invest in extra memory cards and an external hard drive.

©DJI

Drones

Professional cameras
The DJI S1000 can be
fitted with a digital SLR to get some
truly stunning photos

Racing with drones

Drone racing is the new form of aerial combat, and it's big. We investigate this voltage-driven phenomenon

Take any invention or method of conveyancing and transportation from across the ages, and you will find that somewhere, humans have been racing it. From Roman chariots and horses to the first aircraft and internal combustion engines, it wasn't long before we were creating racing circuits as we continued hunting our new fix for adrenaline. It's a long-held belief that warfare and competition are the two elements that advance developments in any area, and drone technology is no different. Welcome to the world of drone racing.

Drone racing is a 21st Century motorsport. A unique and intoxicating combination of PC gaming, gladiatorial motorsport, Hollywood movie effects and, of course, adrenaline. As with any form of competition, the origins of drone racing are unclear. In all probability, it started with a couple of bored guys crashing into each other, then challenging one another to a contest. But just like street racing with cars, drone racing is probably hazardous to bystanders, so recently, drone-racing venues have begun to materialise and, as you'd expect, specialist racing and competition drones are now appearing. So, what are the appeals of drone racing and how do you get started? Is it expensive or, just like motorsport, is the answer to the question "How much?" the inevitable "How much have you got?" We talked to some drone-racing experts to find out more about this 21st Century motorsport phenomenon, and how you can get started with drone racing.

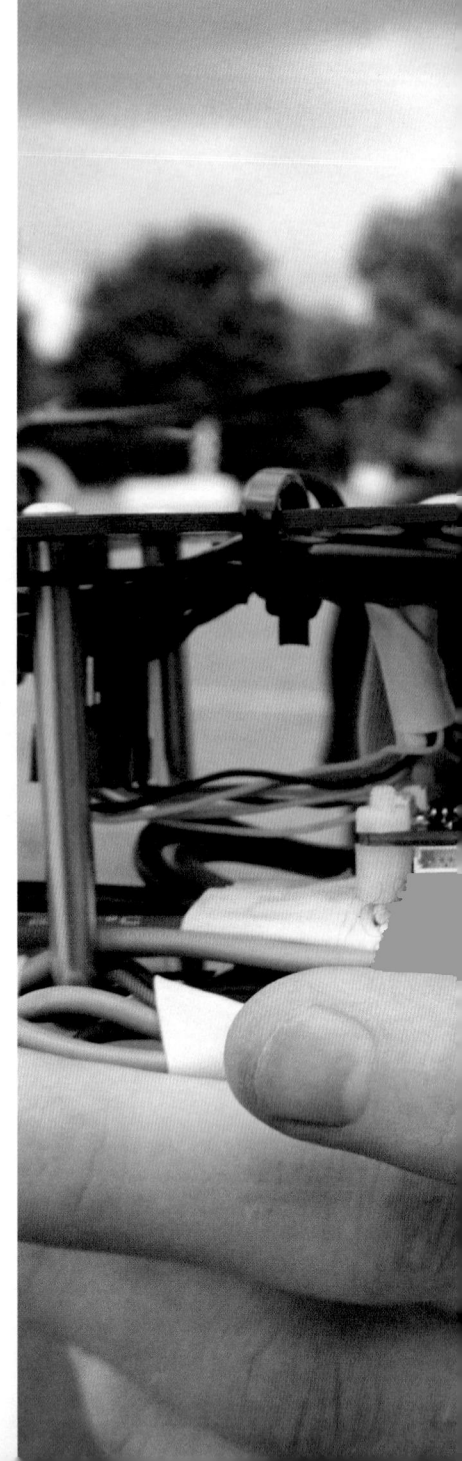

Getting started

Nearly all drones used for racing have quad rotors. Known as quads, they are lightweight, stripped-down machines in the true motorsport tradition, with the absolute bare minimum of equipment. And yes, just like any other form of motorsport, there are varying degrees of machinery, from 'production' classes all the way to the Formula One machines of drone combat. Every drone-racing pilot we spoke to offered the same advice: start with a small, inexpensive drone. The Hubsan X4 is an impressive quadcopter that will allow you to practise a range of flight manoeuvres before you move onto a bigger quad. This is very important for these three main reasons:

1. Like most sports, the very good guys make it look far, far easier than it really is.
2. You will crash a lot when learning to race your drone.
3. Just like motorsport, crashing a full-size machine is both dangerous and expensive.

At the heart of the excitement of all drone racing are the initials FPV. These stand for first-person view, and this is the key to how you will view and experience your drone race. Each drone has an on-board, fixed camera, which transmits back a live video signal to your flying goggles. Because the camera is fixed and not gyro stabilised, you experience the full effect of acceleration, and the roll of the horizon as you bank, twist and turn around the course. The view through the goggles can only be described as akin to the Star Wars speeder bike chase in between trees. Inevitably, you will crash. Just try not to jump or flinch too much on your first impact, and learn to avoid them as you go along.

Once you've mastered flying, it's time to get competitive and own your first full race drone. You have two options:

1. Buy a ready-to-fly (RTF) or almost-ready-to-fly (ARF) quadcopter.
2. Buy parts, such as a frame, motors, props and so on, and build it yourself.

We can't really say which of these options is better for you. If you like building things, the second option is great. For many people, building the quad is half the fun. The other main advantage of building your own quad is that you'll have the knowledge and skills to fix it when you crash. As we've already said, crashing is inevitable. Get used to it.

Start with a small, inexpensive drone, as crashing is inevitable when you begin racing

Most racing drones have quad rotors, which are lightweight and have minimal equipment

Anatomy of a racing quad

If you decide to build your own quad racing drone, each one has a series of essential elements that are needed to be successful. Here's our guide to the vital things you'll need to go drone racing.

- **The frame** What would be called the chassis or fuselage were it a car or an aircraft, drone-racing frames are typically all carbon. Two of the most popular are the Blackout Mini H and the Lumenier QAV250. Both retail online at around $150.

- **Flight controller** Most popular, by far, are the Naze32 Acro and the OpenPilot CC3D. Expect to pay less than $100 for either.

- **Motors and props** It's true that you get what you pay for with motors and props, just like full-sized engines. Cobra engines with HQ Props are the premium brands. If you're on a budget, try Sunny Sky motors with GenFan props. Whichever combination

you choose, order spare props and make sure you have them to hand. They're always the first casualties in an accident.

- **Electronic speed controllers (ESCs)** As the name suggests, they control the power output and keep everything running as it should. They're a bit like the engine-management system for your drone.

- **Battery packs** All Lithium Polymer, these are effectively your drone's fuel tanks. Turnigy Nano-Tech cells are the ones to go for. They employ technology that allows a very high discharge rate. You need this when drone racing, so that when you go for full throttle

to accelerate, your engines are getting enough power at a high enough rate. Be very careful when handling these battery packs. Never leave them unattended when charging, and always check them after a crash. It has been known for crash-damaged packs to burst into flames when subsequently charged.

- **Flight goggles** Fat Shark are the leading brand. Flight goggles are expensive but essential, so look after them. The high magnification screens should always be kept covered when not in use. The magnifying effect of the screens if left in open sunlight can damage them, so always keep them in the protective case.

"It's true that you get what you pay for with motors and props"

Who you can race

There are two main categories for quad drone racing: the Spec Class for beginners and the Open Class for more advanced pilots. As you'd expect, the Spec Class places restrictions on drone power and prop size to help keep things more equal and control costs when you're just starting out. The Open Class is just as the name suggests. This is 'unlimited' air racing, which means anything goes with some truly ballistic machines capable of a mind-blowing 128kph (80mph). Finding someone to race against is more difficult. The sport is still growing, but largely unknown to the broader public. It's a matter of checking in to some of the online forums and finding racers in your area. Websites such as www.fpvracing.tv have drone user groups who are organising events around the world. Search for pilots near you with whom you can hook up.

It's racing, pure and simple

It's that oldest of human emotions: the desire to compete

Humans love to compete against one another. It's how we're wired, and no matter where you go in the world, you'll find somebody organising a racing series for something. From Formula One cars to snails, we'll race it. Most competitive sports involve significant costs, but drone racing allows you to feel the full-on adrenaline of competition without massive expense. Perhaps this will change, but we doubt it. Because even the latest technology is relatively inexpensive, drone racing will probably continue to be cost effective for some time to come. It's in its early stages which, in our view, is the best time to become involved.

How to get involved

Drone racing as a sport is fairly new, so where do you find it?

This is a new global phenomenon. Each country has its own particular take on it right now, from Australians using disused, dockside warehouses to Scottish drone-race clubs arranging events in the Highlands. It's not an underground movement, but you won't find it in the mainstream press. Look online and on social-media platforms to hook up with racers to compete with. We found groups across the world, from Scotland to Australia and across the United States, including Ohio, Los Angeles and Arizona.

Racing with drones

Essential kit

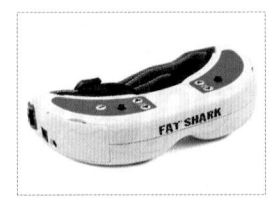

First-Person-View (FPV) goggles Goggles are expensive, but vital to FPV racing. The feed is projected onto the screen and high-quality magnification gives an immersive view of your race.

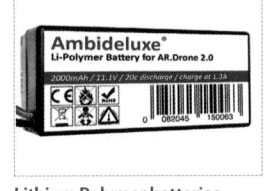

Lithium Polymer batteries These allow very rapid discharge rates, which give motors the rate of power needed to accelerate fast. Quads are capable of 128 kph (80mph) due to them.

Cobra engines Tiny stepless, 8-volt electric engines, just 22.5g (0.8oz).Some have high peak power, but lack midrange, others have lots of torque, or midrange power, for stronger acceleration.

How racing works

There are several types of competition in which you can get involved. Rotorcross is flat-out, side-by-side drone racing. All you need are two or more pilots to form a grid, then you race in real-time around a pre-set course. The winner, quite simply, is the person who crosses the line first. At the time of writing, first-person-view drone-racing series are rather spread out, but with each passing week, there are new meetings being announced online and on Facebook groups across the world.

Drone dragster racing pits two drones against each other in a standing start drag race down a 100 metre track. This is where those high-performance props and that high discharge battery pack really come into their own and can give you an advantage. Unlike automotive drag racing, many drone dragster races count the time from lift off to touch down, with no flying finish. Note that we said 'touch down', not crash. That would definitely not win you the race, nor any future races for that matter!

Finally, we have time trial. Just like special stage rallying for drones, you fly individually, against the clock, with the winner holding the fastest stage time. One of the practical things about a time trial is that there are several online communities that allow you to set up your own time trial and then record your efforts using an on-board camera. Upload your video to the time-trial community, and add your score to a global leaderboard. Each month there is a winner announced in the series.

- **Safety** Be organised. Use tape to cordon off pathways where unsuspecting people may stray into the drone-racing area, and be sure to sign-post the area significantly. It's a good idea to post marshals with two-way radios if your course goes out of sight through trees, so that you can be sure the course is clear. With some drones now capable of speeds of 128kph (80mph) or more, they pose a significant hazard. The people at First Person View in the UK have produced flag and banner kits at a low cost to help get grass-roots drone racing off the ground. They are generally quite happy to help get drone-racing clubs organised.

- **Risk assessment** Health and safety is a boring subject, but a simple, written risk assessment is a good way to bring to your own attention things that might need to be foreseen. Simply make a list of all of the possible things that could go wrong on a sensible level, and write down solutions for them, or courses of action should they occur. It doesn't need to be a huge document, and you don't need to be a firefighting paramedic, but it's well worth doing, if only to help your event run more smoothly on the day.

- **Promote your event** With drone-racing forums and Facebook groups in abundance, spreading the word through social media is the best way to promote your drone-race meeting.

- **A venue** This can be anything from a farmer's field to an old, underground car park or some woodland. Above all, make sure that you have permission from the landowner to be there and race.

Right now is a great time to become involved in drone racing. Like any competitive sport in its early stages, things are advancing very quickly. While some people may think that it's a good idea to sit back and watch before committing time and money, in our view being involved at the beginning of what is almost certain to become a global phenomenon is a far better way. Learning about drone racing by being at the coal face and getting dirty first hand will give you invaluable experience in the technicalities, racecraft and developing winning techniques and strategies that will turn you into a drone-racing champion. You've got to be in it to win it.

"Like any competitive sport in its early stages, things are advancing very quickly"

The sport is growing, so it will no doubt be easier to find people to race with in future

61

Flying for fun

Use your drone to let loose and have fun with friends and family wherever you are

"The technology in modern UAVs means that radio-controlled flying is easier and more accessible than ever before"

Many people see modern drones as something mainly used by filmmakers and hard-core technology geeks. UAVs can be seen as elitist, hard to fly and needing considerable technical skills as well as exceptional hand-eye coordination. In fact, the technology in modern UAVs means that radio-controlled flying is easier and more accessible than ever before. If you're thinking of investing in a quadcopter of your own, but worry that it may be just a fad and will soon be forgotten at the back of the spare room, here are a few ideas on fun things to do with a drone that anyone can try, which will stop you becoming bored with your UAV.

Radio-controlled flying is now easier and more accessible than it has ever been before

©Romeo Durscher / DJI

All the family can fly

Until recently, the best you could expect from any kind of radio-controlled flying device was a scale model helicopter. These could prove almost as difficult to fly as a full-sized helicopter, but without the benefit of the reference points and perspective of actually sitting at the controls, not to mention the most badass way of getting to work. So, while you could possibly manage as the machine was flying away from you, as soon as you bank around to return, everything is reversed and they become even harder to fly. Add in the fact that they have no computer stabilisation, and you will spend a frustrating amount of time crashing and repairing.

Modern UAVs are a lot different. They have multiple rotors, meaning that there is no requirement for a tricky tail rotor to counteract engine torque. Many of them come equipped with first-person-view cameras that actually put you aboard the machine. Plus, most vital of all, they have incredibly complex stability control systems, which give them the ability to hover at a single point in space without the continuous inputs you would normally need in a conventional scale model helicopter.

What this means is that almost anyone can fly a modern drone, opening up the opportunities to share the fun on a wider scale than has ever been the case before. Everyone from the smallest youngsters right through to your most senior family members can try operating the drone without worrying about major damage. You can have a great day of family fun with a drone-flying

competition that will challenge your family to find the greatest drone pilot. And while at first you may need to teach your children how to fly a UAV, frustratingly, it won't be very long at all before they're the ones doing the teaching as you ask them how they actually did that stunning drone move you just witnessed.

We're going to outline some great exercises for all the family to try. They're really good ways of teaching everyone how to fly a drone safely, together with some reminders of ways to help complete beginners stay safe.

First, use GPS mode for maximum protection and so it returns to base. Remember, there is no gentle take-off option. This is deliberate in order to take the drone to a safe hover height. Don't try to hover close to the ground; it simply makes it

harder than is needed at first. Always fly with the propeller guards fitted, especially if everyone else in the family is looking on.

Start with 'tail in' moves. By this we mean that the drone's nose is facing away from you. This makes everything easier, as your left is the drone's left and so forth, and navigating comes quite naturally. Have a contest to hold the steadiest tail in hover, then have a series of practice landings. You can build on this with 'side on' manoeuvres where you get everyone to fly the drone by looking at it side on. Ensure nobody turns sideways to match the drone's orientation. That way everyone can develop the skills needed to operate it from any angle. Fly with a nose-in hover. This will sort out the winners, as that can be the hardest to master mentally.

Everyone in the family can try operating the drone without worrying about major damage

They have incredibly complex stability control systems, which give them the ability to hover at a single point

REC 🔋 📶 🔋🔋🔋🔋

Parrot

"Don't try to hover close to the ground;
it simply makes it harder than is needed
when you start flying"

Become a drone collector

If the UAV-flying passion grips you early on, you'll soon find that owning just one quadcopter isn't enough. As you become more accomplished and your skills grow, you'll soon be casting your eyes around for additional drones. This is where it can become addictive because, while the technology has become more mature in the last few years, it's still a rapidly developing science. Most people within the industry predict that, just like the explosion in mobile-phone ownership, within the next decade a huge number of people will become drone owners. There are several ways to expand your drone collection; here are our favourite ideas on how to develop your UAV army.

First, look at the areas you're not currently active in drone flying, and think of acquiring specialist drones for each task, then learn to become as accomplished as possible in that discipline. Chances are, you may well have a DJI Phantom product. It's the world's bestselling drone, but hot on the heels are new drone models emerging onto the market.

Consider buying drones at different price points for different projects. For example, there are many drones at very low purchase figures that could almost be considered disposable. In the filmmaking industry, they're referred to as 'suicide cameras', as they're genuinely not expected to survive. As long as any camera footage can be recovered, that's what matters. While you may not wish to harm your faithful drones in such a brutal way, having drones like that will give you the confidence to experiment with sending your quadcopter into areas that you may well not wish to risk your more expensive drone model.

If competition is something that excites you, racing drones is a new but rapidly growing sport. You will definitely need to add to your drone collection for this one, and you will almost certainly be building some elements of this yourself.

Be involved in drone development

You may well become fascinated in the technology behind drones and want to know more. While you can learn a significant amount by building your own drone from a kit, there is a limit to how much you can actually learn from existing technology. New drones are arriving all the time, and you can be involved in their development.

Many fresh drone projects are launched through Kickstarter and other crowd-funding platforms, so this is a great place to get the heads-up on what could be the next cutting-edge advancement in UAV development. To compete with industry giants like DJI, many fresh startup drone companies are looking to crowd-funding platforms to generate enough resources to get their project moving.

©DJI

If you don't want to buy a drone like this DJI Inspire 1, you could make your own

Inside drone crowd funding
How crowd funding works and what to look for

Many drone projects are crowd funded. The cutting-edge, global technology lends itself to this method perfectly. If you wish to speculate on a UAV project like this, do it through recognised sources, such as Kickstarter or IndieGogo. They verify that the projects that exist are worth supporting. Most projects offer perks for supporting them, such as special editions or early

delivery. The idea is that, instead of trying to convince one big financial institution to give all the money, they ask lots of people across the world to loan small amounts each. When the project is successful, everyone gets their pledge returned to them in the form of the final product.

It pays to read up on each project and check the protections that are on offer from each platform.

Crowd funding can be difficult to understand sometimes, so it pays to do some research. Often, the developers are only looking for small sums of money from each 'backer'. In return for an up-front pledge of funding, you receive one of the very first UAVs when the design comes to fruition. Several leading filmmakers are actively involved in supporting crowd funding drone projects, so it pays to study what their views are. Filmmakers such as Philip Bloom have backed several successful crowd-sourcing UAV ventures, so it's worth reading his blog on what it takes to see a successful project through to production.

The Zano nano drone, for example, started as a crowd-funding project, and has now reached the point where the designers are ready to ship. Being involved in a crowd-funding drone project can be an exciting way to feel involved in the development and birth of a new UAV. Look carefully at the small print of each project before committing funds.

You will learn an awful lot, not just about quadcopter technology, but also about the stresses of bringing a new product to market and watching the developers strive to be successful. When you receive your first crowd-funded drone, you'll justifiably feel proud of the fact that not only do you own the latest in drone technology, but you helped start a new business and launch a fresh product into the world.

With many youngsters using drones, the next generation is going to grow up with them

Teach the family to fly
Modern drones are the most stable they have ever been

Modern UAVs have sophisticated software and stability controls that make them extremely easy and stable to fly. You can have great fun teaching everyone in the family to fly a quadcopter, but here are our important tips on how to do it safely:

• Always fly with the prop guards on and stay more than a few metres away.

• Fly with GPS mode enabled and allow the technology to help beginners to fly.

• Fly at no more than walking pace until everyone involved becomes confident.

• Remember, less is more. Make drone movements smooth and slow for the best results.

Once you've mastered your drone, you might think about entering drone competitions

Become a UAV aerobatic pilot

As your drone skills reach a high standard, you'll want to push the envelope of what's possible. Just like pilots of full-scale aviation, the limits can be exciting places to be. Welcome to drone aerobatics. Many of the moves achievable by aerobatic or acrobatic drones are similar to conventional aircraft. The best way to learn drone aeros is to research online for how-to videos. There are experts able to give video walkthroughs of each manoeuvre to help get started. Obvious moves like loops and rolls are within reach of many of the smaller, agile drones. But once you've mastered these, it becomes obvious that a quadcopter is capable of far more than this. Acrobatic drones are fast-moving, aerial gymnasts able to undertake moves such as back flips on the spot, upside-down flying and many, many other moves. If an acro-drone is for you, there are specialist drones currently in development that will achieve ever more stunning moves. At some point, perhaps we'll add smoke to them and start the very first formation drone airshow team. Now that would be a project worth supporting.

"When you receive your first crowd-funded drone, you'll feel proud that you helped start a new business and launch a fresh product"

Drones to have fun

Parrot Hydrofoil This mini-drone from Parrot connects to a hydrofoil and can skim across the water at speeds up to 6mph. It's the perfect drone for kids and anyone taking a drone near water.

Parrot Bebop The Bebop is an excellent addition to your aviary, especially for drone acrobatics. The Parrot Bebop has a built-in FPV camera, plus acrobatic ability at a very affordable price point.

Parrot Airborne Tthe Airborne comes in two varieties; Night and Cargo. The Night version lets you activate LEDs on the drone using the FreeFlight 3 app, while the Cargo can attach small payloads.

© Getty, Parrot

Explore with your drone

Drone exploration need not be arduous and physical. Here's our guide to UAV exploration on your doorstep

Drones were invented for exploration. From the early Cold War space satellites that photographed our surrounding planets, through bomb disposal robotics to the latest military search and destroy UAVs, we have been sending drones into situations too risky for humans for many years. Drone technology is now accessible to all of us at a price point that we can only have imagined just a few years ago. And while we may not be able to reach up into the stratospheric levels of spy planes, we now have small, ultra-light quadcopters that let us see our surroundings as never before. We take a look at ways to explore your surroundings and discover new viewpoints of the places we've previously only seen from eye level.

Best drones for exploring

The best drones for investigating new viewpoints are perhaps not the big, half metre diameter octocopters. While they can lift a significant, high resolution camera, there's little doubt that they're far more intrusive than their smaller colleagues. Even a DJI Phantom can generate a significant racket and downdraft, so it pays to give some thought on what type of exploring you may be undertaking. Exactly how you plan to view and record your progress will also need to be considered. If you'd simply like to take in the view and have a virtual stroll around from a unique perspective, then FPV goggles will give a totally immersive feel to your flight. Fat Shark is the leading drone flight goggle manufacturer. While not cheap, they are high quality with high magnification.

If you wish to record your exploration for viewing later, a drone with a gyro stabilised camera will be essential. The standard DJI Phantom comes with a perfectly acceptable built-in camera, while the Phantom Plus offers the ability to add the stunning GoPro

"You must understand what your drone is capable of and practise flying it"

camera. This gives you the option of using the camera away from the drone for other projects without the additional cost of another camera. If you already own a GoPro, this is the best option.

In big, wide open spaces, a 'standard' sized quadcopter will be perfectly fine. In fact if it's a windy day, it's probably for the best. They have more power giving resistance to winds, plus they have longer endurance enabling you to stay flying and investigating for longer. But as technology advances, we're seeing more and more nano-drones appearing, plus UAVs with autonomy.

The Zano nano drone, for example, has tiny dimensions that allow it to literally sit in the palm of your hand. Yet it has a powerful camera capable of transmitting images back to your iOS or Android device via Wi-Fi and has a degree of autonomy and stability unheard of from such a small UAV. Its ability to use a combination of GPS and inertial navigation means that it's almost 'self aware'. Add in infra red sensing and it's able to

'see' obstacles and avoid them, making it a great drone to send exploring.

Lily is another 'self aware' drone that is launching in the summer of 2016. If you wish to film your own exploration and record yourself as you hike across wide open countryside or climb trees, the Lily will focus on you without you needing to be actively involved in flying it. Lily will fly off, hold position and film you as you explore. Perfect for that David Attenborough style 'piece to camera' once you've climbed that hill.

Exploring with drones can be a hazardous business. The view you're trying to achieve means your drone is at risk. Consider choosing a drone at a lower price point that, should it die in the line of duty and never return, won't be too distressing to your wallet. You don't want to lose a DJI Phantom 3 or Parrot Bebop on your first flight. You might also want to invest in a crash pack to protect your drone if accidents occur, and a propeller guard can safeguard against serious damage.

Above: Utilise your drone to gain a new perspective on landmarks in your community

Exploring your neighbourhood via drone can be exhilarating, but check that you're not breaking any laws before you start flying

Start with a clean sheet
Opportunities to explore are all around you

Take a look around your immediate area on foot. Limit yourself to a one mile radius of your home and make a shortlist of places that would be interesting to explore with a UAV. Once you adopt that open-minded attitude, you'll be amazed at all the different places that were previously inaccessible that can be viewed and explored with a quadcopter.

Places that you pass by all the time will become interesting once more when you consider the parts of them that you can now access via UAV. Anything from flying off the edge of a multistory car park to flying up into the tree canopy to watch birds and squirrels in local woodland are all things you've probably seen before, but never from that unique perspective.

© Stacy Garlington / DJI

If you're a keen hiker or traveller, you can use a drone for reconnaissance

Technicalities and legal issues with going UAV exploring

Sending your drone exploring can be incredibly informative and gives you an angle on your environment you've never experienced before. But in your enthusiasm, don't forget several crucial technical, legal and simple common sense elements that are easy to ignore when you're excited at achieving that first unique viewpoint.

Each country has its own rules for drones and many of these apply even if you're flying privately. Be sure to obey the rules regarding your UAV's proximity to others. For example UK rules state that you should be in control of your drone and it remains a certain distance clear of people and within your direct sight. If you're exploring on holiday with a drone, check the regulations there.

If you're sending your drone into an enclosed space, don't forget that all UAVs depend heavily on GPS for their positional awareness and navigational ability. The Return To Base function will not work if your drone loses its positional fix, so your UAV will panic if the batteries run low and it needs to find somewhere safe to

land. Also, don't forget that most drones are still not 'self aware'. They cannot see obstacles and they rely on you for guidance. We talked to one drone operator who was flying off a coastal pier, exploring the ancient timbers. His drone panicked about a low battery and activated its return to base function. All was well as it winged its way in a direct line towards the end of the pier, until just a few feet from home it hit the safety railings and bounced into a salty, corrosive ocean. So before you send your UAV on a mission, consider an escape plan if and when things go wrong.

When exploring, be a good neighbour. Don't forget that not everyone will find the high pitched whine of drone motors and propellers quite so exciting. Many people are worried about invasions of their privacy and indeed some countries, such as France, have quite strict laws on people's right to privacy, even in a public place. As time passes, people will come to accept drones as just part of everyday life, but as a responsible drone owner you should accommodate other people when out exploring, and always ensure you're aware of the laws before you start flying.

Where to explore

You won't need to travel all that far from your home to find some fascinating places to explore with your UAV. Places that you've frequently passed by and are considered familiar take on a whole new dimension when you begin to consider approaching them with a quadcopter. Here are our favourite environments for exploration, many of which will be just a short distance from your home.

A great place to practise exploration is a beach or shoreline. If you're just beginning drone flying, this environment offers a diverse range of things to explore as well as offering you a chance to gradually dip your toes in the water and become more adventurous in a progressive way. You can begin by flying safely along the flat, open beach. Start by flying over to piles of driftwood to become confident before venturing into the

sand dunes and carefully through the tall grasses. Beach huts and fishing boats in storage are a great subject to fly over and see from a new angle. As your confidence grows, start flying out to places that you genuinely cannot reach. At low tide, many shorelines and estuaries have mud flats. If you're confident that you've set up your return-to-base function accurately, you can fly out across areas that humans would simply sink into and yet you can explore them with ease. Once you become an accomplished shoreline explorer, fly out over the sea and underneath old piers to explore wave tops and the pier superstructure. Why not try hooking up with some local surfers and collaborate by shooting a surf video of them in a way they've never been able to before? If you live miles inland or in a large city, urban areas can sometimes be difficult to explore. Local parks sometimes have restrictions on drone flying at

Gaining access to explore

Never easy, here's our tips on how to gain access and explore areas in the right way

In this modern age, with health and safety being the mantra of every security guard, gaining access to some areas can be difficult, but not impossible. It pays to persevere and try to gain permission to access some areas, but it's never easy.

Firstly, don't just try to enter without permission. Not only will you antagonise everyone including security staff, it's potentially dangerous and illegal. Old buildings

are closed off for a reason, generally because there are hazards inside.

On-site staff will rarely be in a position to give permission, so don't ask. Instead, find out who the owners are and approach them. Give them an upside by offering to document the building for them and ask what its future is. You're far more likely to be successful if they can see some benefit in it for them.

© Stacy Garlington / DJI

Reach further
Use your drone to explore
areas that you'd normally
struggle to traverse

the moment, so instead think outside the box. Consider how your local town might look if explored and filmed at a time of day when few people are around. Okay, so it will mean an early start, but just imagine how you could explore your local area early on a summer's morning before the rest of the world awakes. If you're flying away from large groups of people, the chances are that at that time of day you'll be perfectly legal to fly your drone around your local town before everyone else is awake. Just imagine what local sculptures, monuments and other landmarks will look like when explored by UAV. Even if you think

that your local area is not particularly photogenic, don't be disheartened. You could create a Blade Runner-style video, full of gritty, urban, industrial footage. That area of waste ground can be explored without the danger of becoming covered in grime or twisting your ankle on broken concrete and metal.

For full on urban exploration, try and contact owners of old industrial properties. Disused and derelict industrial property is often awaiting demolition and is a fascinating venue for UAV exploration. Getting permission to fly here is crucial, but also sadly quite difficult. Human nature

Although getting aerial shots like this one is great, bear peoples' privacy in mind

is such that when asked the question, most employees will say no, simply because they're worried about the downside of someone getting hurt, either by your UAV or by you hurting yourself inside the building. Do not annoy security guards by breaking into the property. Instead, use your negotiating skills to explain how they can obtain a unique film of the old building before it is either destroyed or refurbished. Many times, you'll be told no, but when you're successful and are given access, you'll be exploring an old building in ways that the people who lived and worked in it never did.

"Perhaps surprisingly, wildlife and animals are generally unperturbed by drones"

If you're lucky enough to have access to a natural environment, you'll never grow bored of drone exploration. Exploring wildlife and nature from an aerial perspective requires a little planning but is perfectly achievable with most UAVs. Again, consider the places that humans cannot go. We don't mean the depths of a volcano or flying over an iceberg, but there are sure to be places nearby that you'd love to see. Being able to fly over the edge of a waterfall, then turn around and view it from 50 feet out in the void is a fascinating viewpoint that is great to share with others.

Perhaps surprisingly, wildlife and animals are generally unperturbed by drones. The Royal Society conducted research on bird's response to drones in their vicinity and over 80 per cent were simply not bothered if you stayed more than four metres away. It's one of the reasons why wildlife film crews love filming from helicopters. The only time birds showed distress was when approached from above, probably because the UAV took on the appearance of a predator such as a hawk. Stay a respectable distance away and don't posture your drone as a predator and most animals are quite happy to allow you into their world.

The single biggest thing to consider when drone exploring is to start with a completely clean sheet and an open mind. The areas, landmarks and locations that you have passed by every day for years are actually interesting to explore when using a UAV. You don't need to be deep in the Arctic or a rainforest to be an explorer – opportunities are all around you.

Best drone to use

DJI Phantom Still considered the industry standard, the Phantom is widely available, and if you go for the GoPro mount, you can use your camera for other things and spread the cost.

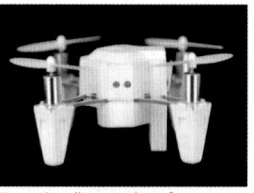

Zano Small enough to fit into the palm of your hand, yet it can stream video to a mobile device. Infrared sensors give it collision avoidance and inertial navigation plus GPS makes it super accurate.

Lily Due summer 2016, the Lily is an autonomous drone designed to follow you. It even floats, so its survival chances are far greater than other exploration drones. Kayakers and skaters will love it.

© Stacy Garlington / DJI

How not to get in trouble

Big or small, all drones are subject to strict regulations when they go airborne

The accessibility of drones has exploded in recent years. Once solely a military venture, drones, UAVs, quadcopters, or whatever you want to call them, are becoming commonplace. Whether it's to help with the shopping or delivering post, a quick breeze through the internet and you can buy (almost) whichever one you like. Crucially, various sets of rules and regulations have been put in place in the wake of this public drone explosion. These guidelines vary from region to region, with some countries more strict than others. The Federal Aviation Administration (FAA) controls everything drone in the USA, while the Civil Aviation Authority (CAA) performs the same role in the UK. Both have devised a series of standards that will allow for close regulation but also the flexibility to accommodate future developments. The FAA came into existence in 1990 and has sanctioned the use of UAVs for firefighting, policing and border control. Recently, due to the boom in consumer availability, it has had to revise its regulations. Normal police officers out on the beat now have the power to arrest anyone who is breaching the rules, allowing the FAA and other governing bodies to extend their legislation significantly. So, what can you do to stay safe and not get into trouble? With so many drones on the market, it can be hard to find the right one. We have compiled a guide to introduce you ten of the coolest drones on the market, which will suit everyone from first-timers to filmmakers. Whether you are a complete beginner and want to learn how to fly or an expert pilot looking for a high-end camera drone to take interesting photos and record video, we've got you covered.

Drone regulations: the operator

Technology aside for a second, what rules do the operator of a drone need to adhere to? Well, more than you might think. The FAA states that if you would like to fly your own unmanned quadcopter, you must be at least 17 years of age and able to pass a specific aeronautical knowledge test. Only then would you be able to obtain your Certificate of Authorization (COA) and be able to take your new purchase to the skies.

The COA currently lasts for two years and will take 60 days to process, but one time certificates are also available for what the FAA describes as 'time-sensitive emergency missions' such as disaster relief. 609 COAs were issued in 2014 compared to only 146 in 2009, so more and more people are becoming interested in what is a fast-growing pastime. Naturally, when in control, you must always avoid any other aircraft and stop as soon as you become a hazard to people or property. And for any showboaters out there,

piloting two UAVs at a time is strictly prohibited. Altitude-wise, you can only pilot your drone up to 121 metres (400 feet) high and no faster than 160 kilometres (100 miles) per hour. Depending on where you live, you'll have to be very aware of the limitations on where you can fly. It is currently illegal to fly UAVs within eight kilometres (five miles) of any airport in the USA, and over national parks and military reservations.

These rules prevent the use of drones in many cities, especially the largest ones which have more than one airport. This has proven to be an essential rule, as a survey undertaken by The Washington Post between 2012 and 2014 found 15 cases where drones were caught dangerously close to other forms of aviation. In Britain, the emphasis on the operator is even stronger, with the CAA stating that any UAV is the complete responsibility of the owner and any failure to comply with the rules could lead to serious criminal prosecution.

Drone regulations: the machine

UAVs come in all shapes and sizes, so regulations need to be flexible so they can represent all drones in airspace. Safety is the primary goal of all aviation organisations, but the guidelines need to be effective and workable, too. The new rules take the rise of commercial drones into account and now allow the free flight of any drone up to 25kg (55lb) in weight. These rules were created by the FAA, whose spokesperson declared them "probably the most flexible regime for unmanned aircraft 55 pounds or less that exists anywhere in the world". In the UK, the CAA understands that a wide range of tools and agencies are available to repair broken drones and requests that all UAVs be undamaged when airborne. Flying at night is also against the law and you're required to keep to the 'line of sight' rule at all times. As you can see, there are still some practical issues that stop drones from taking off, but these regulations don't stop UAVs being incredibly useful machines. As well as having a bit of fun, they can be used for serious measures. It is hoped that small quadcopters can help spread pesticides and water crops in tricky-to-reach areas, as well as helping with mountain rescue and other surveillance roles such as checking the numbers of endangered species.

"In the UK, the CAA understands that a wide range of tools and agencies are available to repair broken drones and requests that all UAVs be undamaged"

Drone regulations: how do I try to stay safe?

No matter how skilled you are there's always a chance of losing your drone when in flight. This is especially so in high winds or heavy rain, as this will only damage the drone and potentially things around it. To improve drone control, a number of clubs have been set up for pilots to meet to discuss their UAV and learn from each other. Several of these societies also provide official training lessons to help you control your drone more effectively. It's definitely worth having your skills as backup if you quadcopter's GPS, compass or altitude control decides to stop working! Another place that drone owners meet is the annual UK Drone Show. Showcasing the

Make sure you stay well clear of people and buildings. FPV doesn't make you crash-proof!

best in UK UAVs, the latest drone technology is on display and the show concludes in an awards ceremony. This is the place to be for anyone who needs hints and tips in understanding drone flight and operation.

Drone regulations: commercial use

As with almost every new gizmo, worldwide firms are seizing the opportunity to jump on the drone bandwagon. Just look at Amazon who is close to introducing the drone delivery system, Amazon Prime Air. But what about the small time entrepreneur who's looking to get some extra business with a little advertorial on their

quadcopter? Well, the CAA states in its official guidelines that for any commercial activity you must get the correct permission. If you don't you could face prosecution, and nobody wants that. So make sure you take the correct measures if you're hoping to give your new business venture a much-needed advertorial boost!

Restaurant chain TGI Fridays got into hot water when a UAV owned by the firm crashed into a diner, cutting her nose open. Meant to be a Christmas publicity stunt, it got the company into big legal trouble and demonstrates the danger of drones – as well as the importance of knowing what you can do – and that mistakes do happen.

There are strict rules governing the use of drones to deliver goods, and any autonomous flight

© Amazon

Enrique Iglesias fractured his hand during a performance after attempting to grab a camera drone

VTOL
Vertical Take-Off and Landing

Modern drones utilise VTOL (Vertical-Take-Off-and-Landing) systems, allowing them to take off from almost anywhere. This has made enforcing laws much trickier as UAVs can now go wherever they want, whenever they want.

Drone regulations: privacy & photos

Privacy is usually a thorny issue but even more so with quadcopters. The majority of drones contain some sort of camera or recording equipment so expect this to be a recurring issue especially in areas where one can expect reasonable expectations of privacy. Most of it is common sense but expect legislation to get even tougher on this topic if it is not adhered to. Taking pictures of military locations is a big no-no, as is filming sports events or music concerts. It can also be dangerous, as popstar Enrique Iglesias found out the hard way after he grabbed a drone during one of his concerts, slicing his fingers open.

Drone regulations: the future

What can we expect in the years to come? With the anticipated pressure from the largest companies around the globe, it is likely that commercial and advertising laws on drones will be relaxed. There is also hope of splitting up the guidelines; at the moment every type, shape and size of drone is lumped in together under one rulebook but as knowledge progresses, this is bound to be tweaked. There is also likely to be a greater difference between laws in rural and urban areas and sparsely and densely populated areas. After all, there are different risks in inner-city London than there are in the Scottish Highlands. In January 2015, a UAV crashed onto the White House lawn initiating a temporary lockdown of the grounds, which goes to show that no matter how many rules and guidelines there are, these drones have the ability to get everywhere and will have to be regulated carefully for the benefit of everyone concerned. So if you unwrap a drone next Christmas, read this guide and you shouldn't go far wrong!

BVR
Beyond Visual Range
Currently, UAVs must be in your line of sight at all times during operation. However as technology increases and user knowledge develops, this is a rule that could be altered, and will benefit people who wish to use drones for delivering items.

Drone regulations summary (CAA & FAA)

....

1. The operator of the drone is legally responsible for every flight and needs to be capable

....

2. Every UAV must be kept in the operator's sight at all times

....

3. You must not endanger people or property

....

4. It is illegal to fly over airports and congested areas

....

5. You must not fly within 50 metres (164 feet) of a person or building

....

6. Any UAV must be registered by the country's governing body to be able to take flight

....

7. Unmanned aircraft must weigh less than 55 lbs. (25 kg)

....

8. The maximum airspeed is 100 mph (87 knots)

....

9. The maximum altitude during flight is 121 metres (400 feet) above ground level

....

10. Pass a recurrent aeronautical knowledge test every 24 months

....

11. Aircraft markings are required

....

12. Be at least 17 years of age

© Corbis

10 amazing ways drones are being used

See how UAVs are deployed for an incredible range of tasks

1. Aiding farmers

A drone is a cheap and effective way to survey large areas of farmland. With a multi-band sensor on a drone, farmers can capture images of crop using non-visible light. This enables them to produce information about the growth of the crop, and deploy fertiliser precisely where it's required. These sensors also reveal crop health, so pesticides can be applied strategically rather than universally.

2. Forecasting the weather

Hurricanes and storms often cause loss of life and damage property, but with advanced warning, the damage can be reduced and lives saved. UAVs, such as AeroVironment's Global Observer, can keep an eye on developing weather conditions in real-time, and supply remote imagery and storm data to assist with life-saving measures. If terrestrial communications equipment, such as cell towers, microwave relays and satellite downlinks, are damaged, the Global Observer's communications payload can keep the emergency services connected, so that they can continue planning evacuations and relief operations, and coordinate their first response. The Unmanned Global Observer can fly for up to six days at a height of 55,000 feet, and cover an area 600 miles in diameter.

"UAVs, such as AeroVironment's Global Observer, can keep an eye on developing weather conditions in real-time"

3. Monitoring country borders

Country borders can be vast areas to patrol using conventional technology, so drones are playing an increasingly large part in this role. The US government now uses fixed-wing Predator class UAVs to scrutinise the Mexican border for illegal traffic. Video is recorded in multiple passes, then the footage is mixed together to spot changes that could indicate the presence of drug smugglers, for example. Agents can then be directed to the appropriate areas.

4. Inspecting oil rigs

Cyberhawk is an aerial inspection company that deploys its drones to perform visual inspections of high-value and high-risk offshore assets. By safely inspecting an active platform's flare (and supporting structures) from a drone's live video feed, they can keep the platform online, saving time and money. The client can then pre-order and manufacture parts to upgrade the structure and keep it running smoothly. All of Cyberhawk's UAV pilots need offshore survival and medical certifications before they can operate a drone in an offshore platform environment.

5. Bringing aid

One of the challenges of transporting medical aid in developing countries is the lack of roads. The Matternet ONE quadcopter carries a central payload box that can be used to transport 1kg of medical supplies over 20km on a single battery charge. Unlike most other drones in this book, Matternet ONE doesn't have a pilot. A doctor can use a mobile app to choose a landing station for the drone, which will then use a cloud-based routing system to find a safe route at a height of between 50-100 metres. It will also plan the route to avoid tall buildings and restricted air-space. This drone is currently in the testing stage, with Doctors Without Borders participating in trial flights.

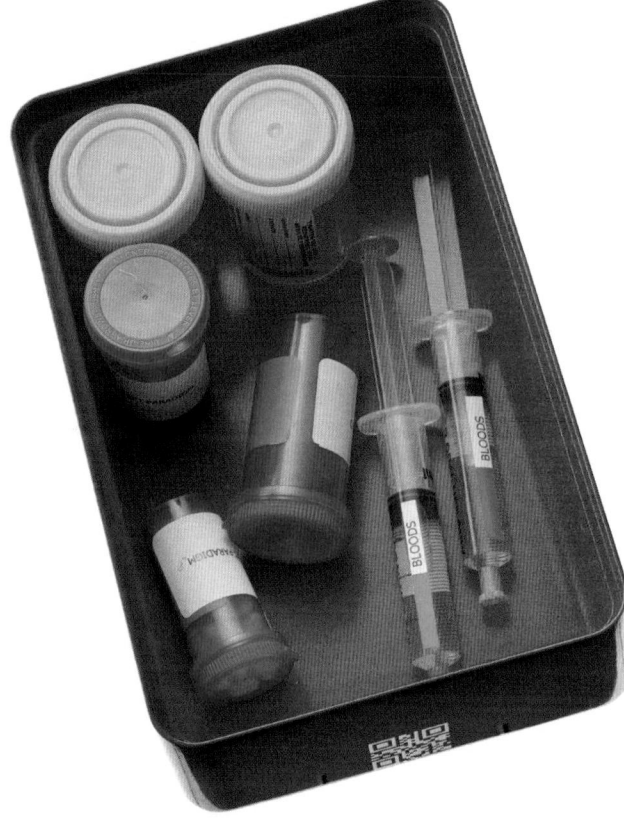

"This drone is currently in the testing stage, with Doctors Without Borders participating in trial flights"

6. Surveying archeological sites

As many archaeological sites are in remote locations, drones are a cheap and effective way to reach and survey these locations. Drones enable scientists to get a bird's-eye view that reveals new information about a site. An md4-200 microdrone UAV was used in Tuketa, in Russia's Altai Mountains, to survey ancient burial mounds (called Kurgans). This resulted in a 3D map of the site that could be used by scientists to measure the volume of the burial mounds. Professor Ian Lindsay from Purdue University used a DJI Phantom 2 to capture aerial data of ancient burial mounds in Armenia.

···

"Archaeological sites are often in remote locations, so drones are a cheap and effective way to reach and survey these locations"

···

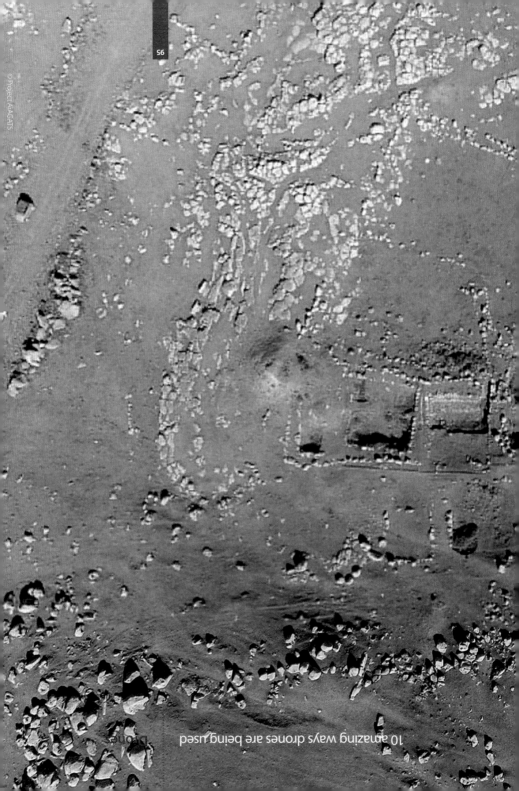

10 amazing ways drones are being used

7. Delivering packages

As the drone started to become a mainstream product, it didn't take long for forward-thinking companies to explore how to integrate them into their businesses. One of the most obvious angles was delivering parcels. The potential in this area is huge, and the prospect of reducing the carbon footprint, man hours or traffic delays has got big players looking at rolling out a drone delivery service. Amazon is currently working on Prime Air to deliver small packages in under 30 minutes, and DHL has started trialling the 'parcelcopter' in Europe.

8. Measuring air quality

Drones can carry a range of sensors to take meteorological measurements, such as temperature, humidity and air pressure. They could also use sensors that detect poisonous particles in the air, as Fire Chief Andy Cashmore explains: "They could look for fibres and heavy metals in the smoke, and that will include asbestos." In China, a drone is being tested as part of the war on pollution. A parafoil helps the drone stay aloft as it glides through smog, spraying chemicals that freeze the pollutants in the air and cause them to fall to the ground.

9. Racing

In abandoned warehouses or car parks, pilots race custom-built multirotor rigs. Many use First Person View (FPV) goggles to navigate their drone around the course via its camera. Craig Jump from Sky View Video has been involved in a consultation with the BBC about developing a drone-racing TV show. He explains: "This is something that's taken off in the last six months, as low-cost kit came in. At night, they race around the tree trunks in forests in the middle of nowhere." Check out indestructible sports drones, visit **gameofdrones.com**.

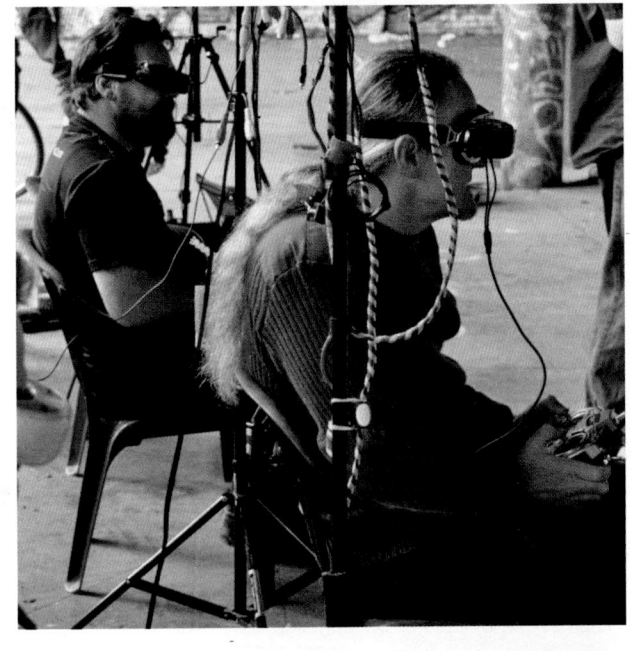

10. Creating art

Drones inspired musicians to include them as components in creative projects. In 2014, John Cale's Drone Orchestra featured a live performance in London's Barbican Centre, in which costumed drones flew above the audience to accompany the music. Pilot Stef Williams told us that the cumbersome costumes worn by the drones "made them really top-heavy – some of them were a complete nightmare to fly, on a par with flying one of the big frames with a Red Epic camera in 40-mile-an-hour winds! But yeah it was good fun!"

How drones are changing the world

How drones are changing the world

We take to the sky to discover how professionals are using drones in a range of amazing ways

Thanks to a drop in manufacturing costs, and rapid advances in technology, drones have flown into many professional and recreational areas in the last few years. In the next few chapters you will discover how drones are being used to help keep firefighters safe, assist rangers in spotting potential poachers, enable news gatherers to report from disaster zones, and keep maps up to date. There are also film makers who are using drones to replace traditional film-making equipment, enabling them to get shots that would be too dangerous and expensive to capture using a helicopter. There's even an insight from a military drone pilot on how drones are being used in intelligence, surveillance, target acquisition and reconnaissance.

We'll also discover how drones are being embraced by the non-professionals, with the advent of drone racing and the impending invasion of throw-and-go flying cameras that will follow and film the users.

Although the term 'drone' has been embraced by popular culture to apply to any unmanned flying device, many of the professionals that we interview refer to them by other acronyms such as UAV (unmanned aerial vehicle), UAS (unmanned aerial system), RPA (remotely piloted aircraft), multirotor, hexacopter and octocopter.

"You must understand what your drone is capable of and practise flying it"

Fighting wars

Discover how UAVs are used to assist the military in the realms of information, Surveillance, Target Acquisition and Reconnaissance (ISTAR)

The commercial and hobbyist unmanned aerial vehicles (UAVs) that are in other chapters of this book can trace their ancestors back to a military source. It was the military who were motivated to research and develop UAV technology, and who had the resources to do so. Some might trace UAVs back to the German-built V1 and V2 flying bombs of World War II, but these 'doodlebugs' were more akin to single-use missiles than today's remotely piloted UAVs.

The term 'drone' has traditionally been used to describe military UAVs. This military connotation has been a concern for some civilian UAV users who we interviewed. Craig Jump from Sky View

Video explains: "One of the reasons I don't like to use the word 'drone' is because people think of military aircraft with the hellfire missiles on them." Jump also found that this military heritage can cause practical problems for civilian UAV users: "The technology is actually classified as dual use, which means it can be used as military technology. So, in certain countries, you need an export licence to take the kit there."

Despite their military heritage, many of today's drones are used for peaceful purposes, such as assisting firefighters in their assessment of an ongoing incident, or looking for refugees adrift in the ocean.

The term 'drone' has traditionally been used to describe military UAVs

Stealth drone
The Boeing Phantom Ray is an American demonstration stealth unmanned combat air vehicle that is currently in development

The Taranis features advanced stealth technologies, propulsion systems and next-generation mission systems

"It was the military who were motivated to research and develop UAV technology, and who had the resources to do so"

However, the modern military still continue to deploy various drones in a range of offensive and defensive capacities. They are also a key driving force towards the ongoing evolution of drone technology. Although drones have been around for a few decades, recent technological developments have seen some dramatic changes, as Chris Cole from Drone Wars UK explains: "Since 2000, the combination of technological miniaturisation and wireless communication has been a real technological leap forward."

Currently, most military drones are propellor driven, like their civilian multirotor and fixed-wing cousins, but that is set to change, as Cole explains: "The Reaper and Predator drones that we have now are comparable to the biplane. We are quickly heading towards faster, more sophisticated and stealthier drones with a low observable profile."

The Lockheed Martin High Altitude Airship is an untethered, unmanned lighter-than-air vehicle

The autonomy debate

One advanced stealth drone is the Taranis, a demonstrator, delta-wing style UAV developed by British defence firm BAE Systems.

Unlike the flying bombs of World War II, modern UAVs are piloted, but have some autonomy. Civilian drones can be programmed to use GPS to follow way points on a map, so they can use their on-board camera to survey wide expanses of forest for wildlife, for example. As military drones can be armed with a deadlier payload, the issue of autonomy is a cause for concern, as Cole explains: "The big issue in terms of military drones is autonomous launching of weapons. There is a big campaign to stop that, and a lot of military people are very wary about moving from what they call having a 'man in the loop' to autonomy in the launching of weapons."

One of those men in the loop is Waqas Tariq, a drone pilot for the Nigerian Airforce: "Bigger UAVs are flown by three people: the mission commander, the pilot who is in control of the drone, and the payload operator who controls the gimble and cameras. 70 per cent of fixed-wing UAV flying is autonomous, with 30 per cent human involvement. Jobs like recording the whole event and moving the cameras are carried out by humans. And obviously the human is the sole person who fires up a weapon on-board."

This 70 per cent autonomy that Tariq mentions is extremely important, because it reduces the chances of human error in relation to keeping the drone safely in the air, where it belongs. Large, fixed-wing military drones can cost millions of dollars, with weapons costing hundreds of thousands of dollars. Chris Cole expands on the advantages of autonomy: "The difficulty is in the communication between the person on the ground and the person in the aircraft. If the aircraft is making decisions in terms of where to fly and how to sense and avoid obstacles, then that is safer, because communication between the pilot and the drone can get snagged or hacked if it isn't encrypted."

UAVs in the British military

As a member of Drone Wars UK, Cole has been keen to monitor the various types of British military drones, as well as their uses: "In its armoury, the UK has the Black Hornet, a very small (five or six-inches long) rotor drone that you can put in your hand. It flies in and out of buildings, and sends a video feed. Then there's a lightweight, fixed-wing drone that soldiers just throw into the air.

"There are also a larger, fixed-wing drones called the ScanEagle and Watchkeeper. The ScanEagle is a prop-driven drone with a ten-foot wingspan that can be catapulted into action by a launcher. The Watchkeeper is capable of flying over two hundred kilometres and sends video feedback to the army." As their names suggest, the drones Cole has listed are used for surveillance and reconnaissance purposes. Military drone pilot Waqas Tariq explains the advantage of using drones in this field: "The Nigerian Airforce uses the UAV in a much more efficient way, because the fighter jets are not able to fly for longer periods of time. But the UAVs can fly for 16 hours." Drones with more offensive capabilities are given more dramatic names, such as the Reaper. Cole tells us: "The Reaper is the armed drone for the RAF. The UK has ten of those in service and each can carry a payload of Hellfire missiles and GBU12 bombs."

Military drones have been around for decades, which is why people like Chris Cole feel compelled to keep asking questions regarding their usage: "Some people in the military accept the need for scrutiny. It's right that there are organisations like ourselves [Drone Wars UK] who are pushing people on this, as there are moral and ethical questions to ask."

The Black Hornet As well as military reconnaissance, the Black Hornet can be used to safely inspect nuclear installations and chemical plants.

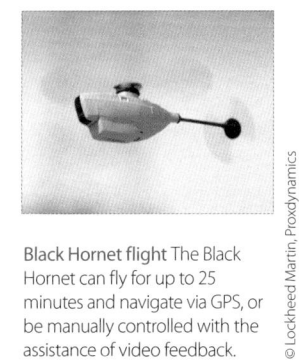

PD-100 Black Hornet This is a nano air-surveillance vehicle that poses little risk to other vehicles or personnel due to its small size and light weight.

Thanks to a pneumatic SuperWedge catapult launcher, the ScanEagle can be deployed without needing a long runway, or from an unprepared site

Black Hornet flight The Black Hornet can fly for up to 25 minutes and navigate via GPS, or be manually controlled with the assistance of video feedback.

© Lockheed Martin, Proxdynamics

Reporting the news

Discover how drones enable journalists to break a story more safely

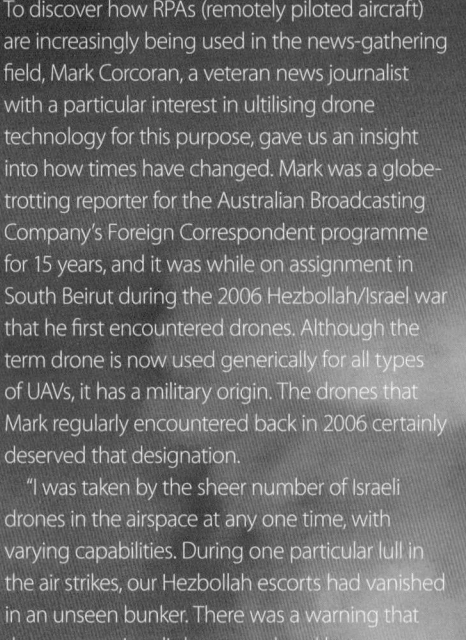

To discover how RPAs (remotely piloted aircraft) are increasingly being used in the news-gathering field, Mark Corcoran, a veteran news journalist with a particular interest in ultilising drone technology for this purpose, gave us an insight into how times have changed. Mark was a globe-trotting reporter for the Australian Broadcasting Company's Foreign Correspondent programme for 15 years, and it was while on assignment in South Beirut during the 2006 Hezbollah/Israel war that he first encountered drones. Although the term drone is now used generically for all types of UAVs, it has a military origin. The drones that Mark regularly encountered back in 2006 certainly deserved that designation.

"I was taken by the sheer number of Israeli drones in the airspace at any one time, with varying capabilities. During one particular lull in the air strikes, our Hezbollah escorts had vanished in an unseen bunker. There was a warning that there was an Israeli drone overhead but we couldn't see or hear it. So our escorts had taken cover. We were left out there and were very exposed. These were fixed wing drones which the Israelis were using for surveillance and for calling in air strikes. I don't believe any of them

were armed, but they were being used for target intelligence purposes for the Israeli attack aircraft."

So how did this experience set him on the path to using drones for news-gathering purposes? "Essentially I took the view that if the militaries around the world could use drones for this kind of work – reducing exposure of their own people to risk while conducting reconnaissance or surveillance – then why couldn't we?"

Learning the ropes

Some television stations and channels are pushing drones to their limits and truly making the most of their potential, but there are still many that need to catch up. Drones are now used by the Australian Broadcasting Company to gather content for TV news broadcasts and current affairs programmes, but the challenge is to find drone operators who also have the camera skills required for news-gathering work. As Mark explains: "There are currently about 200 entities who have permission to operate commercially flying drones in Australia. Only a few of those are what we would deem as suitable for news gathering. What we have found with this emerging technology is a huge emphasis on the platform – on the flying – and surprisingly few of these companies actually meet our standards in terms of what is required for camerawork. We get down to the basic question of 'is it easier to teach a drone operator how to shoot at a professional level or is it easier to teach an existing cameraman how to fly?'"

ABC use many external contractors to fly heavy lift drones in a news-gathering capacity, but there has also been a drive to provide in-house training for ABC employees. Mark fills in the details: "For the training cycle we went for off-the-shelf variants. They offered low-cost, relatively good performance and as they were readily available everywhere we could achieve commonality across the network. We went for the DJI Phantom 2, with a GoPro payload."

So how did senior camera operators fair when taking a drone to the sky? "Flying a small multirotor round the park is one thing, but to do it in a busy location, working to direction and under pressure is another. Initially they were roughly doing about five hours' flying by the end of the two days and this mirrors the qualification for what CASA is now calling the Remote Pilot Certificate in Australia."

© Corbis, Romeo Durscher, DJI

Documenting disaster

So once ABC's camera operators have been trained to fly the Phantom 2, how are both the pilot and the drone used in news-gathering scenarios? Mark explains the process to us: "You have a low cost, simple to operate platform that you can use in high-risk assignments. Then you can use drones for local reconnaissance after disasters. Quite often when you're covering disasters your field of vision is quite limited by debris, wreckage and rubble – so just being able to put a camera up even 40 meters above your position can be of enormous benefit. It's very much used as an occupational and health and safety tool as well as a filming camera platform for news gathering. We used the Phantoms operationally in Vanuatu in March 2015 to follow the big cyclone there."

After Cyclone Pam tore through this archipelago in the Pacific, many of the islands suffered from wide-scale destruction. ABC camera operator Brant Cumming was able to show the impact of this cyclone by recording aerial video footage using the Phantom 2. ABC also deployed a UAV in Nepal, after the April 2015 earthquake killed 7,000 people and injured thousands more. Once again ABC's Brant Cumming used a Phantom 2 to record the devastation in the Gorkha district, the epicentre of the earthquake. This footage was broadcast on a whole range of platforms such as ABC's YouTube channel.

The importance of teamwork

How does ABC's news-gathering drone crew work as a team?

Flying a drone safely while simultaneously capturing high-quality video of a live event would be too challenging a task for an individual. Mark Corcoran explains how a news-gathering drone operating team needs to work together to generate aerial footage in challenging locations: "There is overlap. You've got a dedicated pilot, a second person

can be calling the shots in a busy environment and there is also someone controlling the vicinity of the pilot. With the larger, more complex systems (such as heavy lift multirotors and fixed wing RPAs) you have the camera operator, you have the pilot and you effectively have a director." This division of labour enables the camera operator to follow the director's instructions and capture relevant footage of an unfolding news story, while the pilot keeps the drone safely in the air and manoeuvres it to useful locations. The three-person team controlling heavier RPAs echoes the way military UAV operators fly drones for surveillance purposes. This need for a tight and coordinated team is not surprising, given the cost of a professional drone and its payload. When using a sub-2Kg Phantom 2, a two-person team can suffice. In the image shown here, ABC News camera operator Dave Martin uses a controller to pilot a Phantom 2 which is carrying a GoPro. The live feed from the GoPro is being viewed by the producer Brietta Hague, who uses this visual feedback to direct Dave to capture shots for their Southern Exposure documentary on King George Island, Antartica.

Ahead of the curve

As Australia's national broadcaster, ABC needed to provide live TV coverage of the Australia Day flag-raising ceremony in 2014. Drones provided a useful solution to help cover the event as Mark explains: "There's lots of cameras and prime ministers there and we incorporated the drone coverage quite successfully. Given the location by Lake Bernard Griffin in the capital Canberra it would be inappropriate to have a low-flying helicopter as close as 30 metres to VIPs."

So drones offer ABC's news-gathering teams ways to record informative aerial content for various current affairs and news programmes as well as put eyes in the sky during live broadcasts. As with other professionals in this field, Mark is encouraged by the advance in drone-related technology and where things are heading.

"We are very impressed by the new Phantom 3 Professional quadcopter that DJI has released. It is terrific because it actually incorporates all the modifications we made as add-ons to the Phantom 2s (without any communication from us). The rate of technological development has been extraordinary. It's a bit like laptops and computers; as soon as you buy something it's not completely obsolete, but it's just a case of deciding when you step on the escalator." Thanks to Mark Corcoran, ABC was on the escalator ahead of many others news outlets, which is tangibly reflected in the valuable drone-sourced content in the company's broadcast output.

"We were keen to see how drones would operate in an extreme environment"

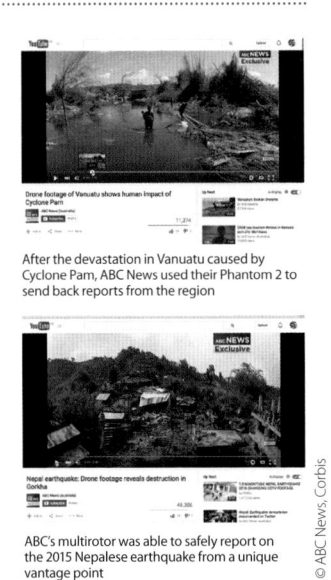

After the devastation in Vanuatu caused by Cyclone Pam, ABC News used their Phantom 2 to send back reports from the region

ABC's multirotor was able to safely report on the 2015 Nepalese earthquake from a unique vantage point

© ABC News, Corbis

Protecting wildlife

Drones take to the sky to help conservationists, fight poaching and assist in a range of wildlife-related projects worldwide

One of the biggest challenges faced by conservationists and those working with wild animals is how to cover the huge areas of terrain occupied by the creatures that they are trying to protect. Certain habitats, such as dense jungles, are also difficult to traverse. Serge Wich is a Professor in Primate Biology at Liverpool John Moores University and his research often takes him into the wild. He is also the co-founder of ConservationDrones. Serge explains how the organisation came to be. "We had been doing survey work in South East Asia and figured that it would be good if there was a more efficient way of doing surveys than just going in on the ground," he told us. "Ground data is great, but it is often very costly and very slow, so we started to look into other options, such as drones."

Initially, the price of drones restricted their use, especially by those from developing countries who were working with wildlife. ConservationDrones was determined to get past this issue: "We started to develop 'do it yourself' drone systems with help from the website

DIYDrones.com. From there, we started to build things and then our first mission was really successful in terms of video and photo footage. So we started to share that with colleagues and set up a website to share our expertise with others." Serge and his colleagues also provide hands-on drone pilot training in a variety of developing countries to help local conservationists and wildlife rangers.

Other technology

So how are drones being used to help protect wildlife around the world? Serge explains some of the projects that ConservationDrones are involved in: "We are flying quite a bit in Sumatra for a whole array of projects that mainly have to do with determining density and distribution of orang-utans. We are also monitoring the forest that they live in to detect logging as soon as it happens." The higher-resolution images sourced by drones enable pilots such as Serge to spot a single illegally logged tree, which helps the authorities protect the orang-utans' habitat. Serge uses drones in his work with other primates, too: "I'm going to Tanzania to see if we can detect chimpanzees nests too. We know that we can do that from the air. We would like to extend that to a savannah setting where chimpanzees occur in very low densities. Traditionally, you would have to cover vast areas on foot to try and locate their nests, whereas if you can fly over a drone system, that would be much easier!"

What sensors or payload are used to locate animals? "At the moment we just use photographs, but we are thinking about other sensors. We are also thinking about detecting chimpanzees at night with a thermal-imaging camera, but that's the next step. We are going to test thermal-imaging cameras in the UK and

then using automatic recognition software to detect those animals. Thermal imaging could also potentially help with protecting rhinos from poachers, as they are sometimes active at night." Poaching of endangered rhinos is such a problem that the Wildlife Conservation UAV Challenge was created to encourage drone-related counter-poaching techniques. Serge Wich is collaborating with a group of students from the Netherlands who have responded to this challenge: "They are trying to develop a user-friendly system for the park ranger. The plan is to get the video analysed on-the-fly so that the ranger looks at a little screen and will see a square around a rhino or a poacher or any other object that needs attention. They can then react much faster to potential threats than they could with other systems."

Thanks to the increasing affordability of UAVs, plus Serge and his colleagues' passion for training conservationists and park rangers how to use these versatile craft, wildlife throughout the globe can be surveyed and protected from a range of different threats.

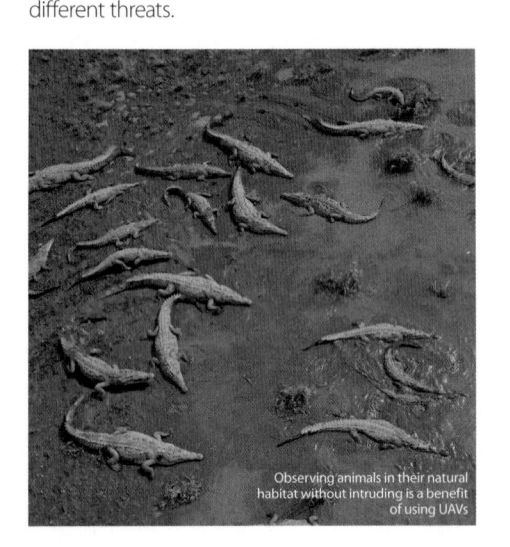

Observing animals in their natural habitat without intruding is a benefit of using UAVs

Drones can allow you to get up close to animals, providing value data to analyse their migratory patterns and actions

Battle of the drones

The pros and cons of different Unmanned Aerial Systems – an expert's view

With a range of wildlife habitats to survey, what's the best type of drone for the job? Multirotor or fixed wing? Serge Wich from ConservationDrones shares the results of his extensive in-the-field experience…

"If you need to cover a small area, a multirotor is fine. And also, where there is no place to land a fixed wing then you are almost forced to use a multirotor, which has vertical takeoff and landing – the open-space requirements are much smaller.

"Most of the multirotor systems have a GPS mode, so whenever you let go of your control stick, that unit will stay at that particular place. It won't drift with the wind and it will remain at that particular altitude, so that's really nice for people who are new to flying. And a lot of the

systems have an automatic landing mode. The planes have that as well, but with the plane of course you always have to land against the wind. So if the wind turns while you are flying then that might lead to a difficult situation.

"There are systems that do take landing into account. The eBee system from senseFly can fly over the landing area and take some information about wind speed and even some visual data. It then figures out the landing path – but those systems come with a much higher price."

© Corbis, senseFly

Aiding in emergencies

We explore the many ways UAVs assist the various emergency services in performing their work more effectively and safely

Although the military have been using drones for decades, it's only in the last few years that drones have been adopted and deployed by emergency services, such as the fire brigade, coastguard as well as the police.

One of the first organisations to add a UAV to their kit list was the West Midlands Fire Service (WMFS) in the UK back in November 2007. As an early adopter of drone technology, WMFS flew a microdrones mD4-200 quadcopter, but they did face a few challenges when using it in the field, as WMFS fire officer Andy Cashmore explains: "It was a little bit temperamental, and there were some limitations in terms of what wind speed it could operate in, battery life, payload capacity and things like that. We used it very effectively in a number of incidents, but we eventually needed to replace it because it reached the end of its logical life cycle."

After finding the best replacement drone, Cashmore's team now use an Aeryon SkyRanger for outdoor work. They also wanted a drone that could operate indoors, so they acquired a DJI Phantom too: "Part of the user requirement was the we may need to operate it indoors, and the Phantom can operate without GPS. It is quite a cheap system and almost disposable, so if we did choose to fly it indoors and it clattered into a wall and got damaged, it wouldn't cost very much to replace or repair it, whereas the SkyRanger might be a little bit more expensive." So in what scenarios does WMFS use its drones? "We tend to use them in distinct areas. The first

area is pre-planning for events. If there are any high-risk premises that either store dangerous goods or carry out dangerous processes, we use the drone to produce some site-specific information for crews, as they get mobilised to incidents at such locations. So we will try to obtain some up-to-date imagery from above the premises, so that they can get a bird's-eye view as they approach the address.

The second area is actually using live imagery when we are responding to incidents. We will go to the incident at the incident commander's request and get whatever data they require in order to bring the incident to a safe conclusion."

> "Most emergency services are still not using drones due to legislation"

The SkyRanger's camera uses three-axis stabilisation to ensure that accurate video is captured even under the most extreme environmental conditions

Drones have been known to assist police officers in locating missing persons or with wide-area searches, and have been very successful in doing so

Safety first

How UAVs help protect emergency personnel

Fire Chief Darrell Hartmann of the Brookings Fire Department in South Dakota, USA, is keen to utilise developing drone technology to keep his crew safe and effective. He is also using this emerging technology in other ways.

How does a drone help you in your work at Brookings Fire Department?
Our drone is a natural fit for the emergency services. During an incident, the commander is seeing live-feed information. And with the situational awareness that this unit can give us, it's just another tool to help us be safer.

What else do you use the drone for?
In hazmat situations, it allows us to send in an expendable tool in order to get up-front information. You can attach a camera so that you can read labels. And if you happen to lose that drone, you can replace it. I do not have to worry about putting one of my personnel at risk.

Do you share the drone with any of the other emergency services?
For the law-enforcement side, if we have a subject barricaded in a structure, we could utilise it to go in to look in the windows, though we would only be able to do those things after we had a judge's court order.

Are there many legal constraints on drone use?
Right now, the biggest hurdle is making sure that we follow our Federal Aviation Authority (FAA) rules. We're in the process of applying for authorisation as an emergency-services provider. There are a lot of people out there in the private sector who have used drones the wrong way, and it makes it more difficult for us.

© AeroVironment Inc, eyyon

How it works

Take off The West Midlands Fire Service began flying with the microdrone md4-200 VTOL (acronym for Vertical Take Off and Landing) UAV.

Checking the fire The video feed appears to show that the fire is out and there's just residual smoke. The IR camera shows that fiery 'hot spots' still remain within the factory.

Upgrade West Midlands Fire Service upgraded to the Aeryon SkyRanger, benefitting from extended flight times and a greater manageability even in windy conditions.

Detecting danger

The drones have proved themselves invaluable when attending fires, as they can obtain information that's not available to the fire crew on the ground. Cashmore gives us a specific example: "We attended a large factory that had caught fire during the night, and the fire had spread to the adjoining buildings. They thought they had got the majority of the fire knocked down and that there was just a bit of smoke and residual heat left in the building, so they were going to scale the operation down. But as soon as we got the drone up there, and used our thermal imaging camera, we were able to identify that there was quite a large area inside the building that was still burning. "

Taking things further

Cashmore is keen to extend the drone's capabilities beyond visual and heat detection: "This is something that we are working closely with Aeryon to develop. We are looking at the possibility of being able to fly into a smoke flume and get real-time data about what is inside. We are looking at a sensor that is capable of detecting gamma radiation, a photo ionising detector for volatile organic compounds, and a multichannel gas detector so that we can influence the information that we give to various partner agencies, and ultimately the safety advice that they then give to the public. The next phase after that is to develop the capability whereby we can fly into the smoke flume, gather a bagged sample of the air and bring it back down to the ground. We would then use our suite of detection identification and monitoring equipment to see what bad chemicals are contained within the sample."

The Ambulance Drone can massively reduce response times, greatly increasing survival rates

Light and mobile
The Ambulance Drone is lightweight, and can be folded down to become a compact medical toolbox to help save lives

"We are currently looking at a sensor that is capable of detecting gamma radiation"

Helping save lives

Discover how drones can increase survival rates

The creation of Alec Momont, the Ambulance Drone is a revolutionary way to respond to medical emergencies. Built using 3D printing techniques and a strong but light carbon-fibre frame, this drone is a glimpse of what might become commonplace in the future. Enabling the emergency services to cut average response times from approximately ten minutes to one minute, by getting the right supplies to people in need so quickly, survival rates could be increased from eight per cent to 80 per cent.

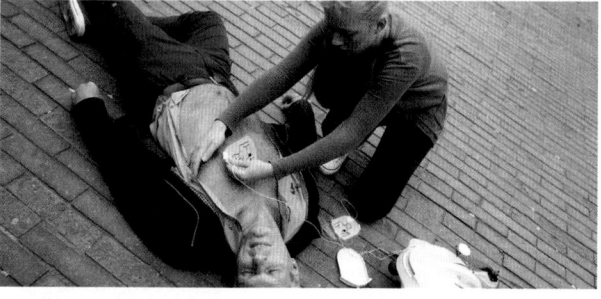

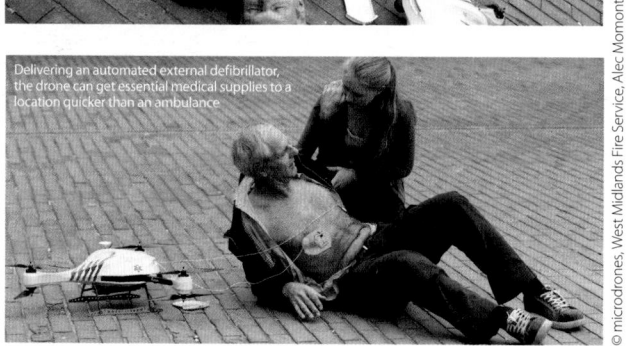

Delivering an automated external defibrillator, the drone can get essential medical supplies to a location quicker than an ambulance

© microdrones, West Midlands Fire Service, Alec Momont

115

Taking photos

Discover how UAVs are used to generate images for a whole range of various photography-related projects

Since the invention of photography, many people have been absolutely fascinated by capturing a bird's-eye view of the world in photographic form. This desire to take aerial photographs was a driving force for many professionals to start using drones and to realise their potential in this market, including Stef Williams of Aerialworx: "I always wanted to take a camera to the sky. I was flying my remote-controlled aeroplanes and trying to strap mobile phones onto them, and then small cameras, which didn't work very well. Then, about four years ago when the quadcopter technology came onto the market, because I was already flying remote-control aeroplanes, it was a natural progression to move onto these drones."

In the early days of multicopter technology, you

couldn't just buy a craft and fly it straight from the box. Early adopters, like Williams, faced many technical challenges with their drone before they could even try to take a camera to the air: "I built my first drone from scratch. When I got my first kit, everything had to be purchased in a mishmash of components. So you'd buy four motors, four speed controllers and a frame, then you attached everything to it. And then you bought a flight controller, and had to connect that to your computer and program everything. My hobby of flying remote-control aeroplanes turned into a job when I attached commercial grade cameras onto these drones." Williams now owns her own aerial company that employs three UAV pilots.

> "Early adopters, like Williams, faced many technical challenges before they could take a camera to the air"

Capturing stills

As well as capturing aerial video for the TV and film industry, Williams is also employed to capture photographs from her multirotor craft. For stills work she sometimes uses an X8 mini octocopter carrying a payload of a Canon 5D digital SLR. We spoke to Williams while she prepared to shoot a series of photos of a manor house to be published in a brochure. How did she approach the challenge of taking professional photos from the air? "To be honest, it's not very different to how we approach a filming job. The main difference is that we haven't got a film crew for this particular one, so we are simply going to turn up at the location. The client told us to just choose a day when the weather is good and we have got good lighting. Then we'll get the drone out. It's a dual-operated drone with one person controlling the camera and the other person flying the drone."

Although this airborne photo shoot sounds like a quick and simple task, some pre-planning is required when using a UAV for commercial purposes. "Before the shoot, you have to set up a cordon. It is quite remote where we are working; there aren't many people present. It's in a private estate, so there are members of the public walking around. We do have to be slightly aware of them, but they have all been informed that there is going to be a drone photographing things today."

Professionals like Williams capture their aerial images and videos using craft and camera payloads that are worth thousands of pounds. At a pre-order price of $499 plus shipping costs, the Lily Camera promises to provide a far more affordable aerial photography solution. This cute-looking quadcopter is touted as a throw-and-shoot aerial camera. Once it's been launched by hand, it will then take to the sky, follow the subject wherever it goes, and shoot stills or video clips of them.

Taking a still from the air still needs the same preparation and materials as shooting film

You can take gorgeous shots from your own area or while travelling from the air, but it comes with its own level of risks

The Lily Camera follows a tracker worn by the subject and can be programmed to follow them from the front or behind, or even circle them as they cycle or snowboard. When it's launched later this year, social-media sites are likely to feature many more aerial photos of people's activities.

With all these cameras in the sky, it's likely to raise the issue of privacy, though Craig Jump of Sky View Video (Scotland) believes that drones aren't a cause for concern: "99 per cent of people that I speak to are fine with it; they are just quite interested in drones. Then there is the odd one per cent who can get very paranoid about privacy and security. People say that you can use drones to look into bedroom windows. If you've ever heard one of these things flying, you'll definitely know if it's outside your bedroom window."

Professional filmmakers, such as the Aerialworx team, have a lot of kit to rig for a shoot, including a 1080 HD live video feed

"This cute-looking quadcopter is touted as a throw-and-shoot aerial camera"

© Romeo Durscher, DJI, Aerialworx

High-angle views
Multicopters are often
used to capture flattering
high-angle views that can
promote a property in a
brochure, for example

Assessing the risks

As a professional UAV pilot working in the UK, Jump has to get special permissions to fly his craft near people. "It's getting easier, because we have a new process that was introduced in February 2015. It is a risk-assessment process where you can put forward a case of flying at reduced distances, so hopefully we're going to get it down to 10m, which will make a big difference. This new policy is called Congested Area Safety Operating Case (CASOC). You must be able to demonstrate that you can fly safely. For example, in one area I might say that I will keep the aircraft below a certain mass. I'll also keep it below a certain speed, so that if there is a failure, then it won't go beyond the 10m boundary. It will have two batteries and four rotors, so if there is a failure, it will still stay in the sky. You have minimised single points of failure."

Professional UAV photographers have to jump through various legal hoops in order to shoot stills or video from the air, but these rules are less strict for UK hobbyists, as Dan Sheills from SkyVue Media explains: "The line is as soon as you earn money, as soon as it becomes commercially viable, that's the point when you need a licence – a CAA qualification. In fact, as a hobbyist, you can have a very large 18kg craft and, if you're doing it as a hobby, you don't need any licence." Hobbyists are still subject to certain rules, though these are rather difficult to enforce, as Craig Jump tells us: "It is very confusing for police to enforce some drone flying. If you don't have a camera on a drone, you can do pretty much whatever you want. It's only really when you put a camera on it that rules and regulations start to come in."

As drones continue to develop and improve, the number of people using them to take incredible aerial photos is bound to increase, so don't be surprised to see them becoming a major part of the photography market.

Stunning landscape shots can be captured if you've got the right equipment

The Lily camera enables you to capture shots as it follows you, or the camera can take the lead and fly ahead

Sense and avoid
Discover the next big leap in UAV technology

The Lily Camera will follow the wearer of a tracker wherever they go, but it cannot detect obstacles, such as trees or power cables, in its path. However, this sense-and-avoid capability could be just around the corner, as Antoine Balaresque from Lily explains: "There are a lot of start-up companies working on sense and avoid. There are also a lot of big companies and research labs working on it too." So, what exactly would sense and avoid mean for UAV users?

Dan Sheills from SkyVue Media is rather excited by the possibilities: "It's when a drone can see an obstacle and it knows to avoid it. It hasn't really been developed so that it's lightweight enough to be put on a craft. It's the technology that is currently being used in driverless cars. A lot of people are researching how to get that technology up onto the craft. That will be a complete game changer, because you could send a fixed-wing drone off and say: 'Right, I want to video the whole route of this power line from this point to this point' and then the drone will be able to follow those power lines. "When the fire service currently sends drones into a house, the drone has to be piloted by a physical person. If it has a sense-and-avoid capability, then you can tell it to just go into the house, and it will find its way in and out all by itself, scanning for people with an infrared camera mounted on it." Until sense-and-avoid technology takes to the air, drones have a variety of safety features. For example, if the Lily Camera is about to hit an object, you are able to press a button and it will stop and then hover while continuing to film you.

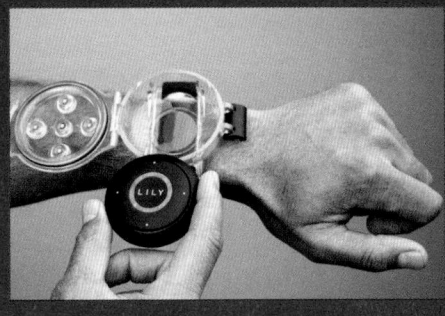

Making films

Discover how drones are changing the way filmmakers (and even their clients approach a shoot

Drones enabled SkyVue Media to see the bigger picture of this off-road track day event for the G4 Challenge group

With the development of drones, filmmakers are discovering exciting new ways to capture distinctive footage for a wide range of film, TV and corporate productions.

While planning a TV commercial, energy company EDF wanted to show the journey of various energy assets in the UK in a single shot. They tasked UK-based SkyVue Media with the job of capturing drone-sourced aerial footage that would blend seamlessly with handheld steadicam footage on the ground, as SkyVue's Managing Director Dan Shiells explains: "That was quite tricky because the shot starts over the back of a house pointing down, and then we tilt up to reveal the horizon. We then pull back over the house, come down the front of it, and zoom right in on an EDF energy van. From there, the steadicam shot takes over, travels down the van, and then we pick up the shot at the other end with the drone, and take it back up and out to the bird's-eye view."

To get the multirotor's footage to line up with the steadicam footage was a challenge, so it took SkyVue's crew a day to get the two aerial shots that would normally book-end the steadicam tracking shot.

Traditionally, a crane-like rig known as a jib has been used to lift a camera so that it can view its subject from a low to high angle. For decades, track rails enabled a camera to follow a moving subject. A little bit of research however, will show you that there are many examples of drones being used to replicate these traditional camera moves. "In terms of tracking, steadicam

The SkyJib range from Aeronavics are heavy-lift multi-rotors used by many professional aerial filmmaking companies

SkyVue Media's stunning video footage would have been more expensive and more dangerous to shoot with a helicopter

and jib, we can do all of these kinds of shots with the drone," Shiells informs us. "With the drone, people tend to think of putting it quite high up in the sky, but if you have a skilled pilot, you can bring it down a metre and a half off the ground to get a nice low shot, and then come out to sweeping wide. We're trying to let potential clients know that this is a very versatile service." The main downside to using a drone instead of a steadicam is the noise produced by its rotors. This can necessitate some post-syncing if the scene features a speaking part.

Before drones were very readily available, film-production companies needed to hire expensive helicopters to get aerial shots. Drones make these type of aerial shots much more affordable. Drones can also bring the camera much closer to their subjects than a helicopter could without risking life and limb.

And it's not just their cameras that these filmmakers are mounting on their drones as Shiells explains: "You can mount different things on them. You can mount a light on one drone to produce some dramatic lighting or to be able to get a light where you wouldn't normally be able to. When filming, lots of clients say that they would like to get a light moving over a car to see its reflections. An easy way to do that is to put the light on a drone."

So taken are clients by the versatility of drones that they are keen to use them in place of more traditional filmmaking kit. Where once a camera operator might have filmed a moving car from the window of an adjacent car, now a drone can be used to track alongside the target vehicle. The client's desire to use drones for everything raises logistical (and stamina-related) challenges for aerial filmmakers such as Stef Williams (pilot and owner of Aerialworx): "Because drones are the 'in thing' at the moment, people just want to use them for everything, so we tend to find that we go through batteries very quickly and have to constantly have them on charge. It's quite demanding and they just go from one shot to the next. Production companies are now giving a lot more thought to how they use drones, whereas in the beginning (two and half years ago) they were just bringing the drone along and saying: 'Let's see what we can do with it'. We would sit around for maybe two or three hours and then do a couple of shots, whereas nowadays we tend to be flat out all day!"

Filmmaking equipment

To produce high-definition, aerial footage for production companies, drone pilots like Williams need to get an expensive array of kit into the air. "The most expensive cameras we have flown to date are things like the Epic Red Dragon with some ultra prime lenses. To get the highest resolution we were filming at a resolution of 6K. The camera costs about £65,000. I think the lenses were about £30,000 and we had another £10,000 of ancillaries on there. Follow focus systems enabled us to zoom in and zoom out. So the overall weight of what we were carrying (the payload) was around 6.8 kg." To keep this high-end production kit safe, Williams used a SkyJib octocopter, manufactured by Aeronavics Limited, a New Zealand based company.

To keep multirotors up for a longer shoot is a key goal for professional filmmakers like Williams, and this involves much research and custom rig building. "We're working on an ultra-heavy lift frame, which is a 1.5-metre octocopter. We've gone for ultra-light components, such as new motors that don't use the old type magnets, so they are a lot lighter. We can lift 8kg for up to 20 minutes, which is a long time. When we were lifting a Red Epic camera with our existing SkyJib heavy lift frame, we got about four minutes' flying time. So it's going to be a luxury when we can fly for 20 minutes. "

Other technology

When flying expensive payloads, professional filmmakers rely on technological developments to protect their airborne assets. Craig Jump from Sky View Video explains some of the key safety features on craft and flight controllers: "The more advanced flight controllers have barometers, which help maintain the craft's altitude. With the basic controller, you spend most of your time on the throttle trying to keep the altitude level, which gets quite difficult. You then have aircraft with ultrasonics that can sense the ground and help keep a specific distance above the ground or obstacles. GPS will give altitude and location data to the flight controller, so when you're doing aerial photography or video you can take your hands off the sticks and focus on what the camera is doing while the aircraft stays in one place." It's clear that crafts such as multicopters are quickly becoming a very valuable tool for the production of films, and have already been used in big-budget Hollywood movies such as Skyfall, Harry Potter And The Chamber Of Secrets and The Expendables 3. As the technology continues to develop and the capabilities of drones continue to be pushed, don't be surprised if the next time you see an incredible aerial sequence in the cinema, it is footage that's been shot using a drone. These lightweight little gadgets could soon replace heavy, expensive cranes and tracks.

SkyVue Media uses an octocopter to safely capture stunning views of a wind farm for energy company EDF

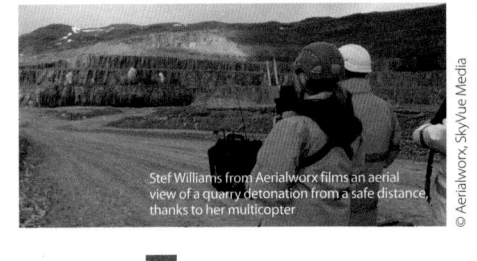

Stef Williams from Aerialworx films an aerial view of a quarry detonation from a safe distance, thanks to her multicopter

© Aerialworx, SkyVue Media

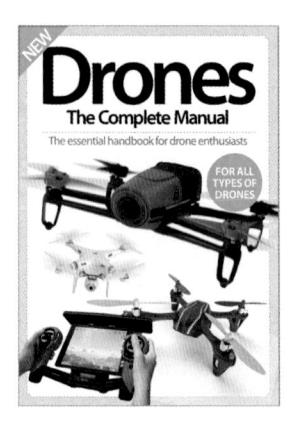

  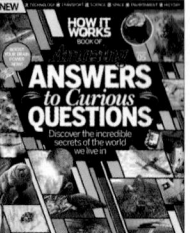